Document-Based Activities for the Middle Grades: Book 1

The American Revolution ★ Westward Expansion ★ Woman Suffrage

★ Implementing CCSS.ELA-Literacy.RH.6-8.2 ★

Written by Barbara T. Doherty and Charlotte S. Jaffe
Illustrated by Karen Birchak

ISBN 978-1-56644-110-0

© 2003 Educational Impressions, Inc.

Printed in the U.S.A.

EDUCATIONAL IMPRESSIONS, INC.
Franklin Lakes, New Jersey 07417

Table of Contents

To the Teacher:
Using Primary Sources

Primary sources are records of events as described by the people who actually experienced the events. These records provide valuable first-hand information and insights into the past. On the following pages you will find letters, historical documents, diaries, photos, examples of fine art, poetry, maps, posters, ads, and other artifacts that are classified as primary sources. Students often look at the study of history as merely a study of facts, dates, and events. They realize that many writings in textbooks are only the author's point of view. However, by using examples of primary sources in the classroom, history will come alive for the students. They will quickly discover the way particular people felt or reacted to a historical event or situation. Through exposure to eyewitness sources, students will change the way they regard the people and events that shaped the history of our nation.

Before You Begin: Introductory Activities

Explain the use of primary sources to your students by having them examine their own primary-source artifacts. Birth certificates, school I.D. cards, report cards, award certificates, lunchroom cards, passports, diaries, yearbooks, and other personal records can be selected. Discuss how these primary sources reveal information about the society in general as well as about the individual. Have students share other primary sources, such as old family photographs. Discuss how fashions, hairstyles, transportation, and settings have changed over the years as seen in the photos. Ask students to conduct an interview with a family member or neighbor who has been an eyewitness to a special historical event or one who can recall a different way of life. Look through old newspapers or magazines and discover differences in the world of advertisement. Discuss the social changes that are reflected in the ads. Visit older homes or buildings in your neighborhood. Contrast them with today's structures. The worksheet on the next page can be used to help students analyze their own primary sources and can be adapted for use with other primary sources throughout the book.

This book is divided into three sections: The American Revolution, Westward Movement, and Woman Suffrage. Each section contains background information on the topic, a variety of primary sources, and challenging activities to help you integrate the artifacts into your curriculum. Through these activities, students will improve their abilities to analyze, create, discuss, hypothesize, and evaluate. These are skills that are required in state standardized tests. They are also skills that are needed by *all* citizens to meet the many complexities of the twenty-first century.

The activities in this book implement the following CCSS:

ELA-Literacy.RH.6-8.2 Determine the central ideas or information of a primary or secondary source; provide an accurate summary of the source distinct from prior knowledge or opinions.

Document Analysis Worksheet

WRITTEN DOCUMENT

1. Type of document: (Newspaper, letter, Map, Advertisement, Other)

_____

2. Physical qualities of the document: (Spellings, Handwriting, Seals, Postmarks, Notations, Other)

_____

_____

3. Date(s) of document: _____

4. Author (creator) of the document: _____

5. List three important facts found in the document.

_____

_____

_____

6. Why was this document written? For what audience? _____

_____

7. What does the document tell you about life in the United States at the time it was written?

_____

_____

_____

8. What information would you like to have that is missing from the document? Write one or more questions to the author.

_____

_____

_____

PHOTO ANALYSIS

1. Study the photograph to form a general impression.

2. Divide the photo into four parts. Study each part to see if you can find details you may have missed.

3. What might you infer after studying the photo? _____

_____

4. What questions do you have? Where might you find the answers to these questions?

_____

_____

_____

Unit I:

The American Revolution

Boston Tea Party, by W. D. Cooper
Source: Library of Congress

The American Revolution: Background Information

The story of the American Revolution began in the New England colonies and spread to the Middle and Southern colonies. Although the colonies were independent of each other when the war began, they all rallied together for the common goal of defeating British tyranny. The ragged Patriots believed that they could win the fight with Great Britain, at the time the most powerful nation in the world. With determination and wise leadership they accomplished their goal, and the thirteen colonies became the United States of America.

The Sons of Liberty—This secret organization was founded to oppose taxes such as those imposed by the Stamp Act. The most famous and active group was located in Boston. Among the members of the Boston Sons of Liberty were Paul Revere, John Hancock, and Samuel Adams. Their symbol was the cone-shaped hat.

The Stamp Act of 1765—Colonists protested the unfair British tax that required them to buy stamps printed in England and to use them on newspapers, pamphlets, and a variety of other business and legal papers. The act was repealed in 1766.

Committees of Correspondence—Throughout the colonies the leading men formed groups known as Committees of Correspondence. Their function was to coordinate the various actions taken against Great Britain.

The Boston Massacre—On March 5, 1770, a mob of colonists with snowballs agitated British soldiers on patrol. A shot was fired by the British. This led to the death of five colonists and the first fight of the Revolutionary War.

The Boston Tea Party—Boston colonists rebelled against the Tea Act, passed by the British Parliament. On December 16, 1773, a group of men disguised themselves as Indians, boarded British tea ships, and threw the chests of tea into the harbor.

The Declaration of Independence—This document was a formal statement by the colonists of their intention to be free from the rule of Great Britain. Thomas Jefferson is credited as the author, but many others contributed their ideas. It was adopted on July 4, 1776. The Declaration of Independence is recognized as one of the greatest documents in the history of humankind.

The Battle of Trenton (December 26, 1776)—General George Washington knew the troops needed a victory to give them confidence. The Hessian soldiers were stationed in Trenton, New Jersey. Washington felt sure that they would be celebrating on Christmas. Hoping to catch them off-guard, he and his men left Valley Forge and marched to Trenton on Christmas night. Small boats ferried about 2,500 men and equipment across the icy Delaware River to New Jersey. The Americans surprised the Hessians and captured many prisoners.

The Battle of Monmouth (June 28, 1778)—General Washington ordered Major General Charles Lee to attack the British troops near Monmouth Courthouse, New Jersey, as they retreated from Philadelphia towards New York City. Lee attacked, but after some fighting ordered a retreat. The British, led by Sir Henry Clinton, counterattacked. Washington arrived in time to lead the men back into battle, but the British forces escaped and the battle was indecisive. Some good did result, however. The Americans showed that they could use their new skills and fight well with their muskets and bayonets.

The Battle of Yorktown (September 28–October 19, 1781)—British General Cornwallis and his troops were trapped by General George Washington and French General Rochambeau on the ground and by the French fleet on the Chesapeake Bay. Cornwallis surrendered at Yorktown after the last big battle of the Revolutionary War.

The Treaty of Paris—Signed on September 3, 1783, this treaty between the United States of America and Great Britain recognized America as an independent nation and was generous to America in many ways.

Famous Patriots:

Benjamin Franklin—Franklin was born in Boston, but he settled in Philadelphia in 1723 at the age of sixteen. Seven years later, he owned his own publishing business. But Franklin's career took many turns. He became an author, statesman, scientist, and diplomat. Franklin took an active role in the fight for independence and in the formation of our new nation.

Patrick Henry—Born in Hanover County, Virginia, Henry became a lawyer in 1760. In 1764, he was elected to the Virginia House of Burgesses and soon became one of its leaders. Henry served as a delegate to both the First Continental Congress and the Second Continental Congress and was the first elected governor of the state of Virginia. He was a skilled orator, and his fiery speeches helped the cause of independence.

John Paul Jones—One of the great Revolutionary War heroes, John Paul Jones is known for his daring attack on a larger British ship, the *Serapis,* on September 23, 1779. When his ship, the *Bon Homme Richard,* drew close to the British ship, Jones was asked if he was ready to surrender. "I have not yet begun to fight," he replied. Jones captured the British ship and sailed it back to France.

Thomas Paine—As a former Englishman, Paine was well acquainted with the corruption of the monarchy rule. He was self-educated and attracted to politics, writing, and debating. Paine used his writing ability to influence other colonists to believe that it was important to be independent from Great Britain. He is best known for his pamphlet *Common Sense.*

Paul Revere—On April 18, 1775, Paul Revere, a Boston Patriot and silversmith, took on the dangerous task of warning the colonists of the impending arrival of British troops. His famous midnight ride helped to summon the Minutemen to fight and allowed John Hancock and Samuel Adams to avoid being captured by the British.

George Washington, Commander in Chief—As a soldier, he had distinguished himself during the French and Indian War. As Commander in Chief of the Continental forces, Washington proved to be a trusted, smart, and compassionate leader. He led the American troops through the battles of the war and sought to alleviate the dire situation at Valley Forge. In 1789 he was unanimously elected the first President of the United States.

The Sons of Liberty

In several of the colonies there were groups of men calling themselves the Sons of Liberty. These men were among the first to call for freedom from British oppression. At first they met and acted secretly. Eventually, as more and more people became convinced of the injustices of the British rule, they met and acted in public. Their early activities included giving speeches, writing letters, publishing pamphlets, organizing demonstrations, and petitioning government officials.

In Boston, the Sons of Liberty included Samuel Adams, Paul Revere, and Dr. Joseph Warren. The award-winning book *Johnny Tremain* tells about a young boy who joins the Boston Sons of Liberty. One of their meeting places in Boston was a certain elm tree, which became known as the Liberty Tree. The area under it was called Liberty Hall. Meeting under a tree gave participants the ability to run in many directions when necessary. The resistance of the Boston Sons of Liberty to British rule soon spread, and dozens of towns in the thirteen colonies formed their own Sons of Liberty. One of the actions of the Sons of Liberty was to call for the Continental Congress to meet, discuss, and coordinate activities.

Source: Library of Congress

To the right is a 1774 British cartoon of an exciseman and some members of the Boston Sons of Liberty.

1. Was the artist in favor of the British or the Sons of Liberty? Give facts to support your opinion.

_____

_____

_____

2. What activity is shown in the background?

_____

_____

3. What is symbolized by forcing the man to drink? What is the drink?

_____

_____

4. Can you tell what had happened to this man before this scene?

_____

_____

The Stamp Act of 1765

Under British control, the American colonists felt that they were not being treated fairly. Because they had no voice in the Parliament of Great Britain, the colonists claimed that they suffered from "taxation without representation." The British insisted that the taxes were fair and that the money was to be used for the benefit of the colonies. The colonists disputed this. They said the money went to Great Britain to enrich itself. On March 22, 1765, the British Parliament passed the Stamp Act. George Grenville, the Chancellor of the Exchequer, had suggested the idea. A special tax was to be added in the form of a stamp. It required the colonists to buy stamps printed in England and to use them on all sorts of papers, including all legal documents, licenses, contracts, newspapers, pamphlets, and playing cards. Because of strong protests by the colonists, it was later repealed.

Analyze the following excerpt from the document:

March 22, 1765
AN ACT for granting and applying certain stamp duties, and other duties, in the British colonies and plantations in America, towards further defraying the expenses of defending, protecting, and securing the same; and for amending such parts of the several acts of Parliament relating to the trade and revenues of the said colonies and plantations, as direct the manner of determining and recovering the penalties and forfeitures therein mentioned.

WHEREAS, by an act made in the last session of Parliament several duties were granted, continued, and appropriated toward defraying the expenses of defending, protecting, and securing the British colonies and plantations in America; and whereas it is just and necessary that provision be made for raising a further revenue within your majesty's dominions in America toward defraying the said expenses; we, your majesty's most dutiful and loyal subjects, the Commons of Great Britain, in Parliament assembled, have therefore resolved to give and grant unto your majesty the several rates and duties hereinafter mentioned; and do humbly beseech your majesty that it may be enacted, and be it enacted by the king's most excellent majesty, by and with the advice and consent of the lords spiritual and temporal, and commons, in this present Parliament assembled, and by the authority of the same, that from and after the first day of November, one thousand seven hundred and sixty five, there shall be raised, levied, collected, and paid unto his majesty, his heirs, and successors, throughout the colonies and plantations in America, which now are, or hereafter may be, under the dominion of his majesty, his heirs and successors:

1. For every skin or piece of vellum or parchment, or sheet or piece of paper, on which shall be engrossed, written, or printed, any declaration, plea, replication, rejoinder, demurrer or other pleading, or any copy thereof; in any court of law within the British colonies and plantations in America, a stamp duty of *three pence....*

Source: Library of Congress

1. Where was the document written?

_____

2. When did the act take effect?

_____

_____

3. Which terms are repeated several times?

_____

_____

_____

_____

_____

4. Patrick Henry's fiery words helped to defeat the Stamp Act. Research and find out what he said.

_____

_____

_____

_____

Anno quinto

Georgii III. Regis.

C A P. XII.

An Act for granting and applying certain Stamp Duties, and other Duties, in the *British* Colonies and Plantations in *America*, towards further defraying the Expences of defending, protecting, and securing the same; and for amending such Parts of the several Acts of Parliament relating to the Trade and Revenues of the said Colonies and Plantations, as direct the Manner of determining and recovering the Penalties and Forfeitures therein mentioned.

WHEREAS by an Act made in the last Session of Parliament, several Duties were granted, continued, and appropriated, towards defraying the Expences of defending, protecting, and securing, the British Colonies and Plantations in America: And whereas it is just and necessary, that Provision be made for raising a further Revenue within Your Majesty's Dominions in America, towards defraying the said Expences: We, Your Majesty's most dutiful and loyal Subjects, the Commons of Great Britain in Parliament assembled,

4 J 2   have

Source: Library of Congress

5. Create a vocabulary list of terms such as *demurrer, pence, rejoinder, revenue,* and *vellum.* Write definitions for them.

_____

_____

_____

_____

_____

_____

_____

_____

_____

_____

6. Divide into two debating teams: American and British. If possible, read the complete document. Use the information in the document to support or oppose the Stamp Act. Hold a class debate.

The Boston Massacre

Source: Library of Congress

The event known as the Boston Massacre took place on March 5, 1770. It began when some boys began taunting the British troops and one of the boys threw a snowball at a British soldier. The soldier became frightened and called for help. Other people became involved, and soon the British began to fire on the crowd. Five people died and many others were wounded. It was the opening fight in the Revolutionary War. To the left is a copy of an engraving representing the tragic event.

1. Who was the creator of this engraving? _____

2. What is happening in the picture? Do you think it is a realistic portrayal of the event? Why or why not? List five things you see in the picture.

_____

_____

_____

_____

3. In your opinion, what was the creator's purpose in creating this illustration of the event? How did it help the colonists' cause?

_____

_____

_____

_____

4. John Adams defended the British soldiers at their trial. Research the incident and judge the results of that trial.

_____

_____

_____

The Boston Tea Party

The American colonists had long objected to paying taxes imposed on them by the British. The objection was especially strong because they had no representation in Parliament. One tax was on tea. To get around this, the colonists bought tea from the Dutch. In 1773, the British passed the Tea Act, allowing the English East India Company to sell tea more cheaply, even including the tax. The British thought that as long as the Americans could pay less for the British tea than the Dutch tea, they wouldn't mind paying the tax. They were wrong.

Colonial leaders in Boston organized a raid on the English ships which were in the harbor; the ships were loaded with the British tea. On the night of December 16, 1773, a group disguised as Mohawk Indians boarded the ships and threw the tea into the harbor. As a consequence, the British closed the port of Boston. This disruption in trade and transportation caused great hardship for the people of Massachusetts. Benjamin Franklin offered to pay for the destroyed cargo, but his offer was refused. In other colonies cargoes of British tea met with similar results. More and more British naval ships and troops were sent to her rebellious colonies.

Below is a transcription of a notice posted in Boston previous to what is now known as the Boston Tea Party.

> Gentlemen,—You are desired to meet at the Liberty Tree this day at twelve o'clock at noon, then and there to hear the persons to whom the tea shipped by the East India Company is consigned make a public resignation of their offices as consignees upon oath; and also swear that they will reship any teas that may be consigned to them by the said Company, by the first sailing vessel to London.
>
> Boston, November 3, 1773
>
> ☞ Show me the man that dare take this down!

1. What is the purpose of the document?

_____

2. Name three facts contained in the document.

_____

_____

_____

3. What does the author hope will happen?

_____

4. What is meant by the last sentence?

_____

5. In your opinion, was the "broadside" effective? Explain.

_____

Paul Revere, the Patriot

In April of 1775, British troops began to march on Boston. The Americans had spies in the British army; the spies learned that General Gage of the British Army planned to arrest John Hancock and Samuel Adams in Lexington and to try them for treason. The Americans flashed signals from the Old North Church to riders who set out on horseback to warn the leaders and the public. Paul Revere was one of those riders. The following is a transcription of a letter he wrote to Dr. Jeremy Belknap:

On Tuesday evening, the 18th, it was observed that a number of soldiers were marching towards the bottom of the Common. About one o'clock, Dr. Warren sent in great haste for me and begged that I would immediately set off for Lexington, where Messrs. Hancock and Adams were, and acquaint them of the movement, and that it was thought they were the objects. I set off on a very good horse; it was then about eleven o'clock and very pleasant. After I had passed Charleston Neck…I saw two men on horseback under a tree. When I got near them, I discovered that they were British officers. One tried to get ahead of me, and the other to take me. I turned my horse very quick and galloped toward Charleston Neck, and then pushed for Medford Road. In Medford, I awaked the captain of the minute men; and after that I alarmed almost every house, till I got to Lexington.
Courtesy of: Marc Schulman, historian—Multimedia

1. What did Dr. Warren want Paul Revere to do?

_____

_____

_____

2. Why was it important for Paul Revere to choose a good horse?

_____

_____

_____

3. Evaluate the success of his mission.

_____

_____

_____

_____

4. Read "The Midnight Ride of Paul Revere," by Henry Wadsworth Longfellow. Compare Revere's account in his letter with the description in the poem. Create a Venn diagram.

Patrick Henry

In 1763 Patrick Henry, a young lawyer in Virginia, shocked those in the courtroom by speaking about the natural rights of an individual. The idea of natural rights later became one of the main ideas of the Declaration of Independence: *We hold these truths self evident, that all Men are created equal, that they are endowed by their Creator with certain unalienable Rights, that among these are Life, Liberty, and the pursuit of Happiness.*

After the hostilities at Lexington and Concord, there were debates in the other colonies about what direction to take. Should those colonies go to the aid of Massachusetts? What would be the consequence of such action? Churches were often used as community gathering places. A meeting was held in St. John's Church in Richmond, Virginia, on March 23, 1775. Many speakers addressed the group. Following the noncommittal speeches of others, Patrick Henry had his turn to speak. The following is an excerpt of his speech:

It is in vain, Sir, to extenuate the matter. Gentlemen may cry, Peace, Peace!—but there is no peace. The war is actually begun! The next gale that sweeps from the North will bring to our ears the clash of resounding arms! Our brethren are already on the field! Why stand we here idle? What is it that Gentlemen wish? What would they have? Is life so dear, or peace so sweet, as to be purchased at the price of chains and slavery? Forbid it, Almighty God! I know not what course others may take; but as for me, give me liberty or give me death!

As the first governor of Virginia, Patrick Henry continued to have influence over the new country. He was one of the strongest voices calling for the addition of the first ten amendments to the Constitution, known as the Bill of Rights.

1. What reaction do you think Henry's speech had on the other members present?

_____

_____

_____

_____

2. Patrick Henry was a gifted public speaker. He was able to influence others by his words. Give two examples of other speeches that have had great influence.

_____

_____

_____

3. Using your dictionary, on another piece of paper define the following words: *extenuate, idle, brethren, clash, gale, endowed,* and *unalienable.*

Benjamin Franklin

A man of many talents and interests, Benjamin Franklin was one of the most important figures involved in the Revolutionary War and the formation of the United States of America. He published the *Pennsylvania Gazette* from 1729 to 1766. In the newspaper he wrote essays on the political situation as well as news articles. He also wrote and published *Poor Richard's Almanac*. A copy of the almanac was in almost every home, giving advice on many topics. Franklin argued successfully for the repeal of the hated Stamp Act. It was during his arguments before Parliament in 1766 that he remarked, "No taxation without representation." Franklin was one of the most active members of the Continental Congress and served on many committees. He helped draft the Declaration of Independence. This Declaration was considered by the British a treasonous act. When John Hancock remarked during the signing of the declaration that the delegates and colonies must stay unanimous, Franklin replied, "We must all hang together, or assuredly, we shall hang separately."

Later in 1776 Franklin went to France to convince the French government it was in their interest to help the Americans against the British. He was well received, and an alliance was formed. By January 1777, the French began sending arms and ammunition to the colonists. By 1780, the French increased their help by sending ships, troops, and money.

In a letter from Boston, Franklin wrote to the Royal governor of Massachusetts William Shirley (1694–1771):

Boston, December 18, 1754

Sir,
I mention'd it Yesterday to your Excellency as my Opinion, that excluding the People of the Colonies from all Share in the Choice of the Grand Council would probably give extreme Dissatisfaction, as well as the Taxing them by Act of Parliament where they have no Representative...dangerous Animosities and feuds will arise between the Governors and the Governed, and every Thing go into confusion.
Source: *The Papers of Benjamin Franklin,* Vol. 5, pp 443-7, Leonard Larabee *et al.,* eds., New Haven and London: Yale University Press, 1962

1. What was the purpose of the letter?

_____

_____

2. What did Franklin fear might happen if the British did not govern more fairly?

_____

_____

3. Of what importance was this letter?

_____

_____

Thomas Paine

Through his writing Thomas Paine greatly helped the cause of American independence. In his writing, Paine was able to state complicated ideas so that they were easily understood by ordinary people. In January 1775 he wrote the essay *Common Sense*. It sold 120,000 copies in just 90 days! *Common Sense* led to much debate and discussion in towns throughout the colonies. Because the war had begun badly for Americans, Paine saw the need for more support from the people. He wrote a series of pamphlets called *The Crisis*. The first was published in December 1776. General Washington ordered it read to his troops before the Battle of Trenton. The profits from Paine's writings were donated to the war effort.

1. Study the cover of *Common Sense* at the right. What can you learn from it?

_____

_____

2. What subjects will be addressed in the essay?

_____

_____

COMMON SENSE;

ADDRESSED TO THE

INHABITANTS

O F

A M E R I C A,

On the following interesting

S U B J E C T S.

I. Of the Origin and Design of Government in general, with concise Remarks on the English Constitution.

II. Of Monarchy and Hereditary Succession.

III. Thoughts on the present State of American Affairs.

IV. Of the present Ability of America, with some miscellaneous Reflections.

Man knows no Master save creating HEAVEN,
Of those whom choice and common good ordain.
THOMSON.

P H I L A D E L P H I A:
Printed, and Sold, by R. BELL, in Third-Street.
M DCC LXX VI.

The following is an excerpt from *The Crisis*. It was read to Washington's troops before the Battle of Trenton.

These are the times that try men's souls. The summer soldier and the sunshine patriot will, in this crisis, shrink from the service of their country, but he that stands it now deserves the love and thanks of man and woman. Tyranny, like hell, is not easily conquered; yet we have this consolation with us, that the harder the conflict, the more glorious the triumph.

1. What was the author's purpose?

_____

2. Why, do you think, has the first sentence become so famous?

_____

3. What is meant by "the summer soldier and the sunshine patriot?"

_____

4. Guess why General Washington wanted this read to his troops.

_____

John Adams Nominates George Washington

In June of 1775 John Adams nominated George Washington for Commander in Chief of the Continental Army. Adams described the nomination in his autobiography. The following is an excerpt:

I had no hesitation to declare that I had but one gentleman in my mind for that important command, and that was a gentleman from Virginia who was among us and very well known to all of us, a gentleman whose skill and experience as an officer, whose independent fortune, great talents, and excellent universal character would command the approbation of all America, and unite the cordial exertions of all the Colonies better than any other person in the Union...Mr. Hancock...heard me with visible pleasure; but when I came to describe Washington for the commander, I never remarked a more sudden and striking change of countenance...

1. Analyze the reasons John Adams used to nominate George Washington to his post. Which reason seems the most persuasive? Which reason seems the most surprising? Explain.

_____

_____

2. Why, do you suppose, did Mr. Hancock show a "sudden and striking change in countenance?"

_____

George Washington sent the following response to his appointment as Commander in Chief of the new army:

Mr. President: Tho' I am truly sensible of the high Honour done me in this appointment, yet I feel great distress from a consciousness that my abilities and Military experience may not be equal to the extensive and important Trust: However as the Congress desires I will enter upon the momentous duty, and exert every power...In their Service for the Support of the glorious Cause: I beg they will accept my most cordial thanks for this distinguished testimony of their Approbation.

But lest some unlucky event should happen unfavourable to my reputation, I beg it may be remembered by every gentleman in the room, that I this day declare with the utmost sincerity, I do not think myself equal to the Command I am honoured with.

As to Pay, sir, I beg leave to Assure the Congress that as no pecuniary consideration could have tempted me to have accepted this Arduous employment, (at the expense of my domestic ease and happiness) I do not wish to make any profit from it: I will keep an Account of my expenses; those I doubt not they will discharge and that is all I desire. George Washington [June 16, 1775]

1. Who was the recipient of the letter?

_____

2. What was causing him distress?

_____

3. Why did he accept the appointment?

_____

4. What payment did Washington request? Why?

_____

5. Write a character sketch of George Washington. Use information from this letter to support your opinion.

George Washington, Commander in Chief

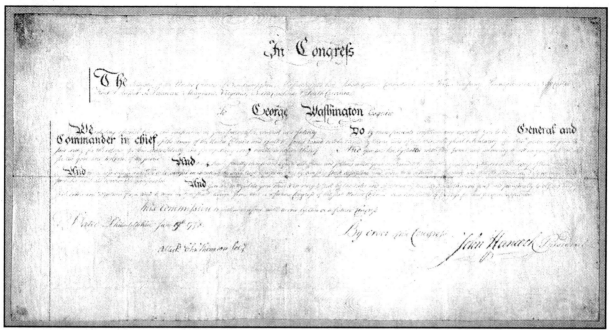

George Washington's Commission as Commander in Chief of the Continental Army

On July 3, 1775, Washington assumed his post. He made his unifying speech:

The Continental Congress having now taken all the Troops of the several Colonies, which have been raised, or which may be hereafter raised for the support and defence of the Liberties of America; into their Pay and Service. They are now the Troops of the UNITED PROVINCES of North America; and it is hoped that all Distinctions of Colonies will be laid aside; so that one and the same Spirit may animate the whole, and the only Contest be, who shall render, on this great and trying occasion, the most essential service to the Great and common cause in which we are all engaged...

3. Why, do you think, did Washington capitalize certain words in his speech?

_____

_____

_____

4. If you were a member of the Continental Army, how might you have reacted to your new commander's speech?

_____

_____

_____

_____

The Declaration of Independence

On May 10, 1776, the Second Continental Congress agreed that the colonies must separate themselves from England. A formal notice needed to be written. The Declaration of Independence was written between June 11 and June 28, 1776, in Philadelphia. Although others helped, Thomas Jefferson is credited with being the author. Jefferson expressed the feelings and convictions of the American people. The document was debated for two days before being adopted on July 4, 1776. It was read to the public outside of what is now known as Independence Hall.

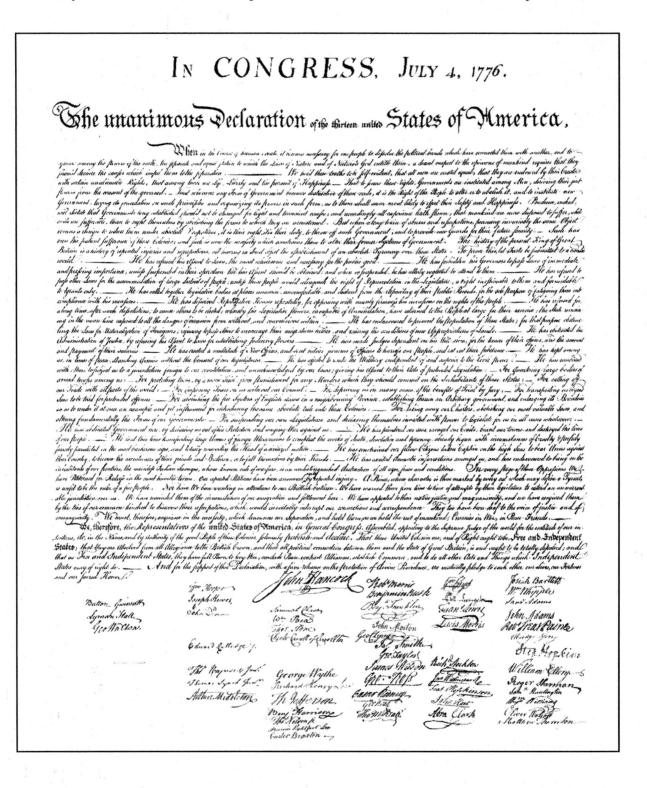

The Declaration of Independence

Transcription of the Preamble:

IN CONGRESS, JULY 4, 1776.

The unanimous Declaration of the thirteen united States of America,

When in the course of human events, it becomes necessary for one people to dissolve the political bands which have connected them with another, and to assume among the powers of the earth, the separate and equal station to which the Laws of Nature and of Nature's God entitle them, a decent respect to the opinions of mankind requires that they should declare the causes which impel them to the separation. — We hold these truths to be self-evident, that all men are created equal, that they are endowed by their Creator with certain unalienable Rights, that among these are Life, Liberty, and the Pursuit of Happiness. — That to secure these rights, Governments are instituted among Men, deriving their just powers from the consent of the governed, — That whenever any Form of Government becomes destructive of these ends, it is the Right of the People to alter or to abolish it, and to institute new Government, laying its foundation on such principles and organizing its powers in such form, as to them shall seem most likely to effect their Safety and Happiness. Prudence, indeed, will dictate that Governments long established should not be changed for light and transient causes; and accordingly all experience hath shewn, that mankind are more disposed to suffer, while evils are sufferable, than to right themselves by abolishing the forms to which they are accustomed. But when a long train of abuses and usurpations, pursuing invariably the same Object evinces a design to reduce them under absolute Despotism, it is their right, it is their duty, to throw off such Government, and to provide new Guards for their future security. — Such has been the patient sufferance of these Colonies; and such is now the necessity which constrains them to alter their former Systems of Government. The history of the present King of Great Britain is a history of repeated injuries and usurpations, all having in direct object the establishment of an absolute Tyranny over these States. To prove this, let Facts be submitted to a candid world.

1. What is the purpose of the document? _____

_____

2. To whom is the document addressed? _____

_____

3. List three facts from the document. _____

_____

_____

_____

_____

4. Identify the names of three signers. _____

_____

5. Was there a signer from the state where you live? If so, who? _____

6. Learn why John Hancock wrote his signature so large. _____

_____

7. Where is the original Declaration of Independence document kept? _____

_____

The Rattlesnake: A Symbol of the Revolution

Even before the Revolution, the rattlesnake was a popular symbol of the American cause. Rattlesnakes are native to North America; they give a warning before they attack; and although an individual rattle might not be heard, acting together, the rattles can be heard by many. Following are examples of the snake motif.

In 1754 Benjamin Franklin's *Pennsylvania Gazette* printed the Join, or Die Flag with the segmented rattlesnake. It was printed to remind delegates at the Albany Congress of the importance of unity among the colonies in light of the impending war with France (French and Indian War).

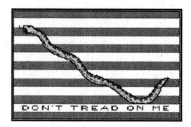

By 1754 the snake was usually shown whole. The Culpepper Flag was probably based on a design called "Rebellious Stripes," which had been created to protest the Stamp Act. It was one of the first flags used by the American Navy. This flag or a variation of it was flown on American ships throughout the Revolution.

The Gadsden Flag is a variation of the Don't Tread on Me Flag. Its field was bright yellow. Designed by Colonel Christopher Gadsden of South Carolina, it was first used in February 1776 by Commander Esek Hopkins, Commander in Chief of the new Continental fleet.

The snake motif was also used on the mastheads of newspapers.

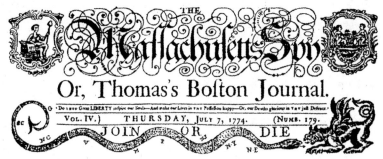

1. Evaluate the use of the rattlesnake as a symbol of the American cause.

_____

2. What do the letters on the Join, or Die Flag represent?

_____

3. What other symbol is used on the masthead?

_____

4. What information is given on the masthead?

_____

5. Compare and contrast the use of the snake in the above examples.

Yankee Doodle

According to tradition, the song "Yankee Doodle" originated during the French and Indian War. American soldiers from the New England area joined with British soldiers to fight at Niagara in New York. In 1750, a British surgeon named Dr. Richard Shuckburgh wrote the song to ridicule the colonial troops, who were outfitted in buckskin and furs. He based it on an old tune. However, the colonial soldiers liked the song and adopted it as their own. There are as many as 190 verses of "Yankee Doodle." It is said that the Americans played "Yankee Doodle" when Cornwallis surrendered at Yorktown.

Here are some familiar lyrics:

Yankee Doodle went to town,
Riding on a pony;
Stuck a feather in his hat
And called it Macaroni.

CHORUS
Yankee Doodle, keep it up,
Yankee Doodle dandy;
Mind the music and the step,
And with the girls be handy.

Father and I went down to camp,
Along with Captain Gooding;
And there we saw the men and boys,
As thick as hasty pudding.

CHORUS
Yankee Doodle, keep it up,
Yankee Doodle dandy;
Mind the music and the step,
And with the girls be handy.

There was Captain Washington
Upon a strapping stallion,
A-giving orders to his men,
I guess there was a million.

1. The words "Yankee Doodle" were supposed to be insulting to the Americans. Use your research skills to determine why the words were demeaning.

_____

_____

_____

_____

2. What is hasty pudding? Make some for your classmates to taste.

_____

_____

3. Create original verses to Yankee Doodle. Perform them with your classmates in a class sing-a-long.

The Battle of Trenton: December 26, 1776

Before Washington's surprise attack on the enemy at Trenton, he feared that the British would try to follow his retreat and attack him in Pennsylvania. To prevent this, he issued the following orders to General William Maxwell, commanding officer of New Jersey's "Maxwell's Brigade":

December 8, 1776

As it is of the utmost importance to prevent the enemy from crossing the Delaware, and to effect it, that all the boats and water-craft whould be secured or destroyed, I do hereby earnestly request and desire that you will take upon you the care and superintendency of the matter. At Tinicum a parcel of boats are to be collected for transportation of the troops under the command of Major General Lee...These boats should be kept under a strong guard. The boats at other places ought, in my opinion, to be destroyed or removed to Tinicum, lest they should be possessed by some stratagem of the enemy.

Source: Old Gloucester Co. and the American Revolution 1763–1778, Gloucester County Cultural and Heritage Commission, 1986.

It was of great importance that Washington's troops drive the British out of New Jersey. Morale was low both among his troops and the general population. Washington decided on a surprise attack. Camped in Pennsylvania, the Patriots had to cross the Delaware River to attack the British. They crossed the ice-clogged river in small boats late on Christmas night. At four a.m. they marched ten miles on icy roads to find the enemy camp. To ensure secrecy, they wrapped wagon and canon wheels in rags. Washington's plan worked; the Patriots had a great victory! The Patriots defeated the Hessians on January 2, 1777, at the second Battle of Trenton and again on January 3 at Princeton. State parks honor the sites of the battles as well as the place where Washington's troops landed in New Jersey. In addition there is a yearly reenactment of "Washington Crossing the Delaware."

1. What specific directives were given in the orders?

_____

_____

_____

2. If you were General Maxwell, what questions might you have had?

_____

_____

_____

3. What, if anything, does this letter tell you about General Washington?

_____

_____

_____

4. What is the connection between the letter to Maxwell and the Battle of Trenton?

_____

_____

_____

Washington at Valley Forge

During the winter of 1777–1778, Commander in Chief George Washington and his ragged troops were stationed in Valley Forge, Pennsylvania. It was a grim winter for Washington's soldiers. They suffered from bitter cold temperatures and lack of food and warm clothing. Washington wrote to Governor George Clinton of the difficulties that the troops faced:

I mean the present dreadful situation of the army for want of provisions, and the miserable prospects before us. …For some days past, there has been little less than a famine in camp. A part of the army has been a week, without any kind of flesh, and the rest for three or four days. Naked and starving as they are, we cannot enough admire the incomparable patience and fidelity of the soldiery, that they have not been ere this excited by their sufferings, to a general mutiny or dispersion. Strong symptoms, however, of discontent have appeared in particular instances; and nothing but the most active efforts every where can long avert so shocking a catastrophe…

Valley Forge–Washington & Lafayette–Winter 1777-78
Copy of an engraving by H.B. Hall   Source: National Archives and Records Administration

1. How did Washington show in his letter that he was a compassionate leader?

_____

_____

_____

_____

2. What was Washington's opinion of his troops?

_____

_____

_____

_____

The Battle of Monmouth

The British, led by Sir Henry Clinton, retreated from Philadelphia, hoping to cross New Jersey and meet with other British forces in New York. Washington wanted to prevent this and at the same time capture British arms and artillery for his own use. On June 28, 1778, he ordered Major General Charles Lee to attack the British troops near Monmouth Courthouse in New Jersey. Lee attacked, but after some fighting, he ordered a retreat. The British, who had received reinforcements, counterattacked. Washington arrived in time to lead the Americans back into battle.

The battle that followed proved to be the longest sustained battle of the war. Both sides suffered heavy casualties. In addition to the fighting, many suffered from the 100-degree temperature of the day. The British left during the night, and the battle remained indecisive. It did prove, however, that the Americans could use their newly acquired skills and fight well with their muskets and bayonets!

As was the custom of the day, many wives accompanied their husbands to battle, providing meals and nursing care. During the heat of the day, one wife, Mary (Molly) Hayes, carried pitchers of water to the thirsty men. She was present when her canoneer husband, John, fell wounded. Molly took his place at the cannon for the remainder of the battle. She is remembered as Molly Pitcher. Although there is much disagreement over the role of Mary Hayes, she was given a very generous pension at the conclusion of the war. In addition, Molly Pitcher was honored by the U. S. Postal Service in 1978 when a special postcard was issued for the 200th anniversary of the Battle of Monmouth.

The map on the left shows troop movements at the Battle of Monmouth, June 28, 1778.

Used with permission, Guggenheim Memorial Library, Monmouth University, West Long Branch, New Jersey

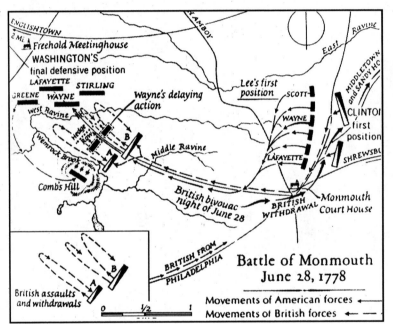

Battle of Monmouth
June 28, 1778

Movements of American forces ◄——
Movements of British forces ◄— —

Examine the map and answer the following questions.

1. What generals fought under Washington's command?

_____

2. Name three types of information shown on the map.

_____

_____

_____

3. In your opinion, what was the importance of this victory for the Americans?

_____

_____

John Paul Jones: The Battle at Sea

John Paul Jones, a native of Scotland, came to America as a young man and was commissioned first lieutenant in the Continental Navy. His first ship was the *Alfred.* In 1776, he was promoted to captain and given command of the sloop *Providence.* On his first cruise aboard the *Providence,* he captured sixteen British ships.

In 1779, Jones was put in command of the *Bon Homme Richard,* named in honor of Benjamin Franklin. He and his crew sailed to England on a mission to raid British shipping. On September 23, 1779, Jones's ship encountered the *HMS Serapis.* The British ship blasted the *Bon Homme Richard,* causing it to lose fire power and gunners. But when the British captain asked Jones to surrender, Jones replied, "I have not yet begun to fight!" Jones and his men eventually won the bloody battle at sea.

Source: Library of Congress

1. In your opinion, why has John Paul Jones's statement, "I have not yet begun to fight," lived on as one of America's most famous historical quotations?

_____

_____

_____

2. What can you learn about the battle from studying this picture? How close were the ships?

_____

_____

_____

3. Research to find out why John Paul Jones is known as the "Father of the American Navy."

_____

_____

_____

Off Scarborough

The poem "Off Scarborough," written by Bret Harte (1836–1902), first appeared in *Scribner's Monthly* in August 1878. It describes the battle between the *HMS Serapis* and the *Bon Homme Richard* from the point of view of an unnamed member of the crew. The eighth and ninth verses give a true account of an event that helped turn the tide of the battle. In the tenth and final verse we learn that the narrator died in the battle.

Source:
SeacoastNH.com

VIII

Then a thought rose in my brain,—
As through Channel mists the sun. —
From our tops a fire like rain
Drove below decks every one
Of the enemy's ship's company to hide or work a gun:
And that thought took shape as I
On the "Richard's" yard lay out,
That a man might do and die,
If the doing brought about
Freedom for his home and country, and his messmates' cheering shout!

IX

Then I crept out in the dark
Till I hung above the hatch
Of the "Serapis,"—a mark
For her marksmen!—with a match
And a hand-grenade, but lingered just a moment more to snatch
One last look at sea and sky!
At the lighthouse on the hill!
At the harvest-moon on high!
And our pine flag fluttering still!
Then turned and down her yawning throat I launched that devil's pill!

Bret Harte

1. What mission did the sailor in the poem complete?

_____

_____

2. Explain the metaphor and the personification in the last line of Verse IX.

_____

_____

3. Keeping in mind when this poem was written and the year in which the battle took place, surmise why Harte chose this battle as the subject of his poem.

_____

_____

Note: This is not a primary source, but it gives a good idea of what it felt like to be at the scene.

Cornwallis Surrenders

The Battle of Yorktown, Virginia, is often called the last major battle of the Revolutionary War. General Cornwallis of Great Britain led his troops to Yorktown hoping to be joined by the British Navy. General Washington and his army moved southward. General Washington's men were joined by French ground forces led by General Rochambeau and by naval forces in the Chesapeake Bay commanded by Admiral de Grass. The French fleet bombarded the British Navy, and Cornwallis was surrounded. His troops lacked food and ammunition. On October 19, 1781, he surrendered to General Washington.

Surrender of Cornwallis at Yorktown, Virginia
Copy of lithograph by James Baillie
Source: National Archives and Records Administration

Here are some excerpts from the diary of Ebenezer Denny, written in October 1781. Denny was a soldier from Pennsylvania. The diary entries describe the Battle of Yorktown and the surrender of Cornwallis at Yorktown.

15th—Heavy fire from our batteries all day. A shell from one of the French mortars set fire to a British frigate; she burnt to the water's edge, and blew up—made the earth shake. Shot and shell raked the town in every direction. Bomb-proofs the only place of safety.

17th—In the morning, before relief came, had the pleasure of seeing a drummer mount the enemy's parapet, and beat a parley, and immediately an officer, holding up a white handkerchief, made his appearance outside their works; the drummer accompanied him, beating. Our battery ceased. An officer from our lines ran and met the other, and tied the handkerchief over his eyes. The drummer sent back and the British officer conducted to a house in rear of our lines. Firing ceased totally.

19th—Our division man the lines again. All is quiet. Articles of capitulation signed. Detachments of French and Americans take possession of British forts...

1. Find out the meaning of *parapet* and *parley*.

_____

_____

2. Write a paragraph describing the surrender in your own words.

_____

_____

_____

_____

3. Compare the British surrender of 1781 with a military surrender in more modern times.

_____

_____

The World Turned Upside Down

Surrender of Lord Cornwallis, painted by John Trumbull
Source: National Archives and Records Administration

1. Look at the painting of the surrender. What do you notice about the flags?

_____

_____

_____

2. What feeling do you have about the surrender after studying the painting?

_____

_____

_____

When Cornwallis and his troops surrendered, tradition says that the British band played the song "The World Turned Upside Down." (Some historians doubt that this is true.)

The World Turned Upside Down

If ponies rode men and grass ate cows,
And cats were chased into holes by the mouse,
If summer were spring and the other way around,
Then all the world would be upside down.

3. Analyze the meaning of the song. Why was it appropriate? How did Great Britain's world turn upside down?

_____

_____

_____

The Treaty of Paris of 1783

In 1783, a treaty of peace between the United States of America and Great Britain was signed in Paris, France. This treaty gave recognition to the existence of the United States. The United States sent Benjamin Franklin, John Adams, and John Jay to Paris to meet with the British commissioners. As a provision of the treaty, Britain gave up the thirteen colonies and the Northwest Territory. The treaty also secured fishing rights in Newfoundland for American fishermen and asked for fair treatment for British Loyalists who remained in the United States.

Tuesday's Post Continued.

DEFINITIVE TREATY between GREAT-BRITAIN and the UNITED STATES of AMERICA, signed at Paris, Sept. 3, 1783.

In the Name of the most holy and undivided Trinity.

IT having pleased the Divine Providence to dispose the Hearts of the Most Serene and Most Potent Prince George the Third, by the Grace of God, King of Great Britain, France, and Ireland, Defender of the Faith, Duke of Brunswick and Lunenbourg, Arch-Treasurer, and Prince Elector of the Holy Roman Empire, &c. and of the United States of America, to forget all past Misunderstandings and Differences that have unhappily interrupted the good Correspondence and Friendship which they mutually wish to restore, and to establish such a beneficial and satisfactory Intercourse between the two Countries upon the Ground of reciprocal Advantages and mutual Convenience as may promote and secure to Both perpetual Peace and Harmony; and having for this desirable End already laid the Foundation of Peace and Reconciliation by the Provisional Articles, signed at Paris on the Thirtieth of November, 1782, by the Commissioners empowered on each Part, which Articles were agreed to be inserted in and to constitute the Treaty of Peace proposed to be concluded between the Crown of Great Britain and the said United States, but which Treaty was not to be concluded until Terms of Peace should be agreed upon between Great Britain and France, and his Britannick Majesty should be ready to conclude such Treaty accordingly; and the Treaty between Great Britain and France having since been concluded, his Britannick Majesty and the United States of America, in order to carry into full Effect the Provisional Articles abovementioned, according to the Tenor thereof, have constituted and appointed, that is to say, his Britannick Majesty, on his Part, David Hartley, Esq. Member of the Parliament of Great Britain, and the said United States, on their Part, John Adams, Esq. late a Commissioner of the United States of America at the Court of Versailles, late Delegate in Congress from the State of Massachusett's, and Chief Justice of the said State, and Minister Plenipotentiary of the said United States to their High Mightinesses the States General of the United Netherlands; Benjamin Franklin, Esq. late Delegate in Congress from the State of Pennsylvania, President of the Convention of the said State, and Minister Plenipotentiary from the United States of America at the Court of Versailles; and John Jay, Esq. late President of Congress, and Chief Justice of the State of New York, and Minister Plenipotentiary from the said United States at the Court of Madrid, to be the Plenipotentiaries for the concluding and signing the present Definitive Treaty; who, after having reciprocally communicated their respective full Powers, have agreed upon and confirmed the following Articles:

Source: Library of Congress

Terms of the Treaty

The following are two important provisions of the Treaty of Paris:

TRANSCRIPTION OF ARTICLE I

His Brittanick Majesty acknowledges the said United States, viz., New Hampshire, Massachusetts Bay, Rhode Island and Providence Plantations, Connecticut, New York, New Jersey, Pennsylvania, Delaware, Maryland, Virginia, North Carolina, South Carolina, and Georgia, to be free, sovereign, and independent states, that he treats with them as such, and for himself, his Heirs, and Successors, relinquishes all Claims to the Government, Propriety, and territorial Rights of the same, and every part thereof.

TRANSCRIPTION OF ARTICLE VII

There shall be a firm and perpetual Peace between his Brittanick Majesty and the said States, and between the subjects of the one, and the Citizens of the other; wherefore all Hostilities, both by Sea and Land shall from henceforth cease; all Prisoners on both Sides shall be set at Liberty, and his Brittanick Majesty shall, with all convenient Speed, and without causing any Destruction, or carrying away any Negroes, or any other Property of the American Inhabitants, withdraw all his Armies, Garrisons, and Fleets from the said United States, and from every Post, Place, and Harbor within the same; leaving in all Fortifications the American Artillery that may be therein; and shall also order and cause all Archives, Records, Deeds, and Papers belonging to any of the said States, or their Citizens, which in the Course of the War may have fallen into the Hands of his Officers, to be forthwith restored and delivered to the proper States and Persons to whom they belong.

1. Judge the generosity of the treaty towards the United States.

_____
_____
_____
_____
_____
_____

2. Explain the importance of the provisions in these two articles.

_____
_____
_____
_____
_____
_____
_____

3. Obtain a copy of the entire Treaty of Paris. Read the other articles to learn more details of the settlement agreement.

Unit II:

Westward Expansion

Across the Continent: Westward the Course of Empire Takes Its Way
Currier and Ives (Frances F. Palmer, 1868)
Source: Currier and Ives

Westward Expansion:
Background Information

Why did people move west? Some desired adventure, but most Americans set out to obtain land and find better opportunities. The first westward movement in the United States was across the Appalachian Mountains. People began to settle in the area between the mountains and the Mississippi River during the 1830s. Explorers such as Daniel Boone and Davy Crockett opened new paths for the pioneers, who followed them along the frontier. The second large western settlement was in the region known as the Far West, which lies between the Rocky Mountains and the Pacific Ocean. This took place in the 1840s, although some small settlements in the area had been started earlier. These areas later became the coastal states of California, Oregon, and Washington and the mountain states of Idaho, Colorado, Utah, Arizona, Nevada, Wyoming, and New Mexico. The third migration, in the 1850s, was to the region that lies between the Mississippi River and the Rocky Mountains—the Great Plains.

The Louisiana Purchase—By a treaty signed on April 30, 1803, the United States bought 827,000 square miles of territory from France for about fifteen million dollars. Not only did the United States double in size, it also gained unthreatened use of the port city of New Orleans and the Mississippi River for travel and trade.

Lewis and Clark Expedition—Meriwether Lewis and William Clark were instructed by President Jefferson to explore and map the lands west of the Mississippi River. The most important goal of the expedition was to find a practical route to the Pacific Ocean. Before leaving, Meriwether Lewis was given instruction by President Jefferson in botany, astronomy, surveying, and other sciences. Forty-five men and six tons of supplies left St. Louis, Missouri, on May 14, 1804. They reached the Pacific coast in November, 1805. Lewis and Clark mapped the area and described the many new animals, plants, and bodies of water they discovered. Many places are named in their honor.

Fur Trappers and Traders—Fur trappers and traders were among the first white men to explore the territory west of the Mississippi River. Often alone or in pairs, these men blazed trails through the wilderness of mountains and prairies. They discovered by trial and error the best places to ford the rivers and find drinking water. These trappers and traders often had information helpful to mapmakers. In addition, they knew about the different Indian tribes of the areas. The trading outposts they built grew into towns and cities.

Trail of Tears—In 1830, the United States Congress passed the Indian Removal Act, which required the Cherokees to leave their homes and move west. Many Americans opposed the law and tried to change it. However, in 1838 the United States government forcibly removed more than 16,000 Cherokee men, women, and children from their homes in Georgia, Tennessee, Alabama, and North Carolina and sent them on a brutal journey to a relocation site in Oklahoma. Thousands of Cherokee people perished as a result of the government action. This tragic event became known as the Trail of Tears.

Oregon Trail—First used by trappers and traders in 1841, this was the longest of the overland routes used by pioneers going west in the 1800s. The trail extended 2,000 miles across deserts, prairies, mountains, and rivers between Missouri and Oregon. During the six-month trip travelers endured extremes of weather, Indian attacks, and disease. So many successfully reached their destination that a territorial government was formed in 1843.

Gold Rush—Gold was discovered at Sutter's Mill in California in 1848. The news spread quickly, and people came from all over to search for riches. Small settlements grew into cities almost overnight. The population of California grew so much that it was granted statehood. Another gold rush took place about ten years later in Colorado with similar results. A third gold rush occurred in 1896, when gold was discovered in the Klondike.

The Pony Express—Pony Express riders delivered the U.S. mail from April 1860 to October 1861 between Missouri and California. The Pony Express was designed to deliver the mail as fast as possible. Riders rode for seventy-five miles, changing horses every fifteen miles. They earned $100 a month, riding in all kinds of weather both day and night. The completion of the cross-country telegraph connections meant that the Pony Express was no longer needed.

The Homestead Act—The Homestead Act was enacted on May 20, 1862. It gave title to 160 acres of public land to those who were 21 and would settle the land for five years in return for a small fee and the promise to make a few improvements. Applicants had to be the head of a household and either a citizen or in the process of becoming a naturalized citizen. Homesteaders could shorten the process after 6 months by paying $1.25 for each acre; they still had to build a home and cultivate the land.

The Transcontinental Railroad—By a law passed in Congress in 1862, two railroad companies were given the responsibility of building a railroad that would extend the railroads of the East all the way to California. This was a huge construction project with far-reaching effects. The Central Pacific Railroad started laying track in 1863, going eastward from San Fransisco. The Union Pacific Railroad began in 1865, laying track westward from Omaha. Work was completed on May 10, 1869, when the two lines met at Promontory, Utah. A special ceremony was held celebrating this accomplishment. This was the first transcontinental railroad in the world. The completed railroad opened huge territories for settlement.

The Louisiana Purchase of 1803

TREATY
BETWEEN THE
UNITED STATES OF AMERICA
AND THE
FRENCH REPUBLIC.

THE President of the United States of America, and the First Conful of the French Republic, in the name of the French people, defiring to remove all fource of mifunderftanding relative to objects of difcuffion mentioned in the fecond and fifth articles of the convention of the 8th Vendemiaire an. 9, (30th September, 1800,) relative to the rights claimed by the United States, in virtue of the treaty concluded at Madrid the 27th of October, 1795, between his Catholic Majefty and the faid United States, and willing to ftrengthen the union and friendfhip which at the time of the faid convention was happily reeftablifhed between the two nations, have refpectively named their plenipotentiaries, to avit, the Prefident of the United States, by and with the advice and confent of the Senate of the faid ftates, Robert R. Livingfton, minifter plenipotentiary of the United States, and James Monroe, minifter plenipotentiary and envoy extraordinary of the faid ftates, near the government of the French republic ; and the Firft Conful, in the name of the French people, citizen Francis Barbe Marbois, minifter of the public treafury, who, after having refpectively exchanged their full powers, have agreed to the following articles :

The Louisiana Purchase was one of the best real estate bargains of all time. President Thomas Jefferson acquired the land from France for a total of $15,000,000. It added about 828,000 square miles of land west of the Mississippi River to the United States territory at the cost of about four cents an acre! With this one purchase, the United States doubled in size! The treaty (there were actually three separate treaties) was signed by Robert Livingston and James Monroe in Paris on April 30, 1803. The American negotiators had planned to purchase only the port of New Orleans and the Floridas. New Orleans was important because it controlled the trade on the Mississippi. To their surprise, Napoleon offered the rest of the Louisiana Territory as well. The Americans quickly signed the agreement.

1. Read the preamble to the cession treaty and rewrite it in present-day form on another sheet of paper. In what ways is it different?

2. Define *plenipotentiary.*

_____

_____

_____

3. The complete treaty of cession contains ten articles. Find a complete transcript of the treaty. What rights are given to France under the Articles? What rights are given to the United States? Present your findings to your classmates.

_____

_____

_____

_____

4. What is the tone of the treaty?

_____

5. Create a map that shows that the Louisiana Territory doubled the area of the United States and gave the nation control of the Mississippi.

Document-Based Activities for the Middle Grades: Book 1

Louisiana Territory

After the Louisiana Territory was purchased by the United States from France, Congress passed an act that gave the President authority to take possession of the territory and provided for the safety and rights of the people living there. This is a transcript of a portion of that act:

An Act to enable the President of the United States to take possession of the territories ceded by France to the United States, by the treaty concluded at Paris, on the thirteenth day of April last; and for the temporary government thereof.

Be it enacted by the Senate and House of Representatives of the United States in Congress assembled, That the President of the United States be, and he is hereby authorized to take possession of, and occupy the territory ceded by France to the United States, by the treaty concluded at Paris, on the thirteenth day of April last, between the two nations; and that he may for that purpose, and in order to maintain in the said territories the authority of the United States, employ any part of the army and navy of the United States, and of the force authorized by an act passed the third day of March last, intituled "An act directing a detachment from the militia of the United States, and for erecting certain arsenals," which he may deem necessary; and so much of the sum appropriated by the said act as may be is hereby appropriated for the purpose of carrying this act into effect; to be applied under the direction of the President of the United States.

Sec. 2 And be it further enacted, That until the expiration of the present session of Congress, unless provision for the temporary government of the said territories be sooner made by Congress, all the military, civil, and judicial powers, exercised by the officers of the existing government of the same, shall be vested in such person and persons, and shall be exercised in such manner, as the President of the United States shall direct for maintaining and protecting the inhabitants of Louisiana in the free enjoyment of their life, liberty, property and religion.
APPROVED, October 31, 1803.

1. List the rights that are being protected.

_____

_____

_____

_____

2. Who has the authority to protect the people of the Louisiana Territory?

_____

_____

3. Pretend that you and your family reside in the Louisiana Territory. What are your hopes and concerns about the change in government?

_____

_____

_____

_____

The Corps of Discovery

In 1803 President Jefferson commissioned Meriwether Lewis to form an expedition to explore the western lands. Lewis called the expedition the Corps of Discovery and chose William Clark as his co-commander. One aim of the expedition was to learn about the geography of the region, especially to find out if there was a water route from the Missouri River to the Pacific Ocean. Another goal was to become acquainted with the native peoples they met along the way.

This map is one of many made by the Corps of Discovery. It shows the routes taken while crossing the Continental Divide. Study the map carefully, then answer the questions.

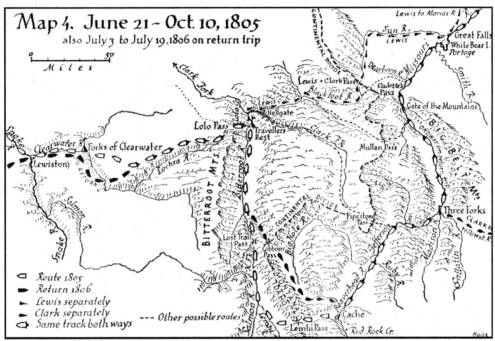

Source: Journals of Lewis and Clark. National Archives and Records Administration

1. What do the dates on the document represent? _____

2. Parts of what U.S. state(s) are included on the map?

_____

3. From this map what do you know of the routes taken?

_____

_____

_____

4. What was the importance of this document at the time? What is the importance now?

_____

_____

_____

5. What types of information are given on this document?

_____

_____

William Clark's Journal

Below is an excerpt from one of William Clark's journal entries. It is said to be his most famous entry. Read Clark's comments and observations and then answer the questions.

Ocian in view! O! the joy.

Later that night, Clark added to his journal:

Great joy in camp we are in view of the Ocian, this great Pacific Octean which we been So long anxious to See, and the roreing or noise made by the waves brakeing on the rockey Shores (as I Suppose) may be heard distictly. William Clark, November 7th, 1805
Source: National Archives and Records Administration

William Clark   Meriwether Lewis

1. What is the date of the document?

_____

2. Although they were still twenty miles away, Clark believed they had reached their goal. What was that goal? How did he feel when he thought they had reached it?

_____
_____
_____
_____

3. What can you learn about Clark from this entry?

_____
_____
_____

4. In addition to the ocean, what other physical features are mentioned?

_____
_____
_____

5. Research and find out how long it had taken the Corps of Discovery to reach this point.

_____
_____
_____

6. In your opinion, what was the importance of the journey of the Corps of Discovery to America?

_____
_____
_____

Fur Trappers and Traders

Fur trappers and traders were among the first to head west. In 1825 advertisements like this one were placed in the newspapers of St. Louis, Missouri. After you have studied the ad, answer the questions.

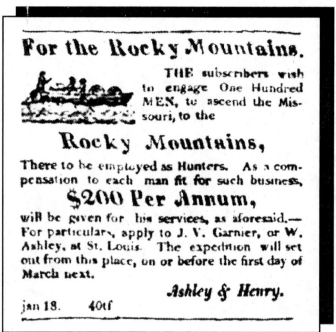

1. Who placed the ad?

_____

2. What is the purpose of the ad?

_____
_____

3. What pieces of information are in the ad?

_____
_____
_____
_____

4. How did ads like this help the westward expansion of the United States?

_____
_____
_____
_____

5. What does this ad tell you about life in America at this time?

_____
_____
_____
_____

The Life of a Fur Trapper

This page appeared in the October 17, 1868 edition of *Harper's Weekly*. It shows events in the life of a fur trapper. Choose one of the illustrations and write a short story about it.

Courtesy of *Harper's Weekly*

Trail of Tears

As the population of Georgia increased, Native American lands were taken over by the state. In 1830, over the objections of many Americans, the United States Congress passed the Indian Removal Act. It meant that the Cherokee Nation, who lived peacefully in western Georgia and had become farmers, ranchers, and good neighbors, would be forced to move west. President Andrew Jackson quickly signed the bill into law. He added:

My Friends,
Circumstances render it impossible that you can flourish in the midst of a civilized community. You have but one remedy within your reach, and that is to remove to the west. And the sooner you do this, the sooner you will commence your career of improvement and prosperity. *Andrew Jackson*

For several years, the Cherokee tried to fight the law in federal courts, but in the end they lost. In 1838, more than 16,000 men, women, and children were taken from their homes to makeshift camps and then forced to march nearly a thousand miles to Oklahoma. The journey was brutal, and thousands of Cherokees died along the way. The route they walked is known as the "Trail of Tears."

Private John G. Burnett of the 2nd Regiment, 2nd Brigade—Recollections of the Indian Removal, 1838–39.

One can never forget the sadness and solemnity of that morning. Chief John Ross led in prayer and when the bugle sounded and the wagons started rolling, many of the children rose to their feet and waved their little hands good-by to their mountain homes, knowing that they were leaving them forever. Many of these helpless people did not have blankets and many had been driven from home barefooted.
Courtesy Marion Co., Arkansas Historic Geneological Society

Jane Bushyhead, a Cherokee girl, wrote to her friend Martha just before the Cherokee were ordered to leave their homes. Her father had tried unsuccessfully to change the Indian Removal Act.

Red Clay Cherokee Nation
March 10, 1838
Beloved Martha, If we Cherokees are to be driven to the west by the cruel hand of oppression to seek a new home in the west, it is very uncertain that I will ever have the pleasure of seeing you. My father is now in Washington City. He was one of the delegates who went to Florida last October. We do not know when he will return.
Source: Danny Farrow, rosecity.com

Use a separate sheet of paper to answer the following questions.
1. Describe the tone of President Jackson's remarks to the Cherokee. Was the move really good for them? Explain.
2. Some people tried to aid the Cherokee as much as possible. John Ross and Davy Crockett were two friends of the Cherokee. Report on ways that they helped.
3. How do you think John Burnett felt about his job as a soldier on the Trail of Tears?
4. How would you have felt if you were a soldier? If you were a Cherokee?
5. Pretend that you are Jane Bushyhead. Write a letter to a friend explaining the problem of the Indian Removal Act.

The Rush to California

In January 1848 James Marshall discovered gold at Sutter's Mill in California. Although Sutter tried to prevent the news from spreading, it wasn't long before the "gold rush" to California began!

Copy of Daguerreotype: James Marshall at Sutter's Mill, 1852

On March 15, 1848, a short article appeared in *The Californian,* a San Francisco newspaper. It was the first news of the gold discovery that would change the nation.

Gold Mine Found. In the newly made raceway of the Saw Mill recently erected by Captain Sutter on the American fork, gold has been found in considerable quantities. One person bought thirty dollars worth to new Helvetica, gathered there in a short time. California, no doubt, is rich in mineral wealth, great chance here for scientific capitalists. Gold has been found in almost every part of the country.

1. Analyze the above article. Guess why the newspaper minimized the discovery.

_____

_____

_____

2. Research to find out what and where New Helvetica was.

_____

_____

_____

3. How might the settlement of the West be different if gold had not been discovered?

_____

_____

4. Research the origin of the California Gold Rush. Who was John Marshall?

_____

_____

Mining for Gold

Source: Currier and Ives

The miners used a variety of tools to dig out and separate the gold from the sand and gravel. Because gold is heavier than sand, when the mixture is washed and the water drained away, the gold remained at the bottom. The Currier and Ives lithograph above depicts several methods the miners used to find gold. Examine it closely.

1. Research the tools and other equipment by the forty-niners. Create a glossary defining the terms.

_____

_____

_____

_____

_____

_____

_____

_____

2. Find an example of a cradle and a long tom in the painting. Explain how they were used in the pursuit of gold.

_____

_____

_____

California or Bust!

In 1849 David Leeper left Indiana for the gold fields of California. His journey across the continent took months and was filled with adventure and hardship. Although he found some gold, Leeper returned home in 1854 and became a writer. The following is an excerpt from his memoir of the journey:

On February 22, 1849, our party set of six set out in two covered wagons. The oldest was twenty-five, the youngest seventeen. We were determined to reach "California or bust!" St. Joseph, Missouri Was our objective point on the frontier it was very crowded. The only transportation for crossing the Missouri was a big clumsy flatboat our wagons rolled on board. We saw many castaway articles on the road that people threw out to lighten their loads. Many draft animals perished and all were footsore. The mountains had rough roads and difficult passages some wagons dropped out completely. Game was by no means plentiful. We saw Chimney Rock and Court House Rock in the distance. When we got there, we carved our names on Chimney Rock. Near the Bear River, we saw a band of Shoshone or Snake Indians they were migrating, too, along with their families.
Source: *The Diary of David Leeper,* Connie and Peter Roop, Benchmark Books

1. How did they cross the Missouri River?

_____

2. Why did they see many castaway items on the road?

_____

3. Describe the condition of the animals in your own words.

_____

4. Research and locate the places and landmarks mentioned in the excerpt.
5. Research and report on the Shoshone Indians.

The following is a letter from Lucetta Rogers to her brother Enos, who lived in Connecticut. She had just joined her husband in California.

September 5, 1858
Our city has been all excitement about New diggings on Frazier River. Hundreds have left good Buisness to start wher gold could be got faster than in the city are now Sitting on the banks of Frazier River waiting for the river to fall. It must be very easy work if not profitable waiting. many have returned to the city to seek their Old buisness and are now Wiser if not Richer men gowing to Frazier River was a house hole word Everybody seemed to be gowing but the excitement has subsided and we are now again quiet.
Source: *So Much to be Done,* University of Nebraska Press

1. Why, do you think, did Lucetta's husband go to California?

_____

2. Why was there excitement in the city in which she lived?

_____

3. Why were hundreds "sitting on the Frazier River?"

_____

4. Rewrite the letter, correcting the spelling and the grammar.

The Oregon Trail

The Louisiana Purchase opened up a huge area for westward expansion. The trip west was too long and too dangerous for any family to experience alone; therefore, wagon trains were formed. The first large migration occurred in 1843 when more than 900 emigrants set out on the difficult journey along the Oregon Trail. At over 2,000 miles, the Oregon Trail was the longest overland route. It began in Independence, Missouri, and went all the way to Oregon City, Oregon.

Below is the engraving *Emigrants Crossing the Plains,* by H. B. Hall, Jr., 1869. Study the picture carefully.

Source: Library of Congress

1. What adjectives would you use to describe the people in the painting?

_____

_____

_____

_____

2. Describe the condition of the animals.

_____

_____

_____

_____

3. Estimate the number of wagons in the train.

_____

4. Who is riding in the covered wagon?

_____

_____

5. Guess why some people were walking.

_____

_____

6. Select a person in the painting and tell about the journey from his or her point of view.

_____

_____

_____

_____

_____

Crossing the Plains

The following are excerpts from the memoirs of a woman named Harriet Palmer. They describe the six-month journey she took with her family along the Oregon Trail when she was eleven.

Source: Denver Library

...In our home, in Illinois, in the early fifties, there was much talk and excitement over the news of the great gold discoveries in California—and equally there was much talk concerning the wonderful fertile valleys of Oregon Territory—an act of Congress giving to actual settlers 640 acres of land...

...The loud voices of the drivers as they yelled and whipped up the oxen, the jogging of the wagons through the surging waters and over the quicksands, the memory is with me yet...My mother kept the two youngest with her always in "Mother's wagon." Her health was not very good, and she had dreads and fears, but hoped she would live to get to Oregon. Fate willed it otherwise, and being frail and weary with the long journey, she fell a victim to the cholera, so prevalent that year on the plains, leaving her sorrowing family to grieve for her...

...The old emigrant trail hold many hard experiences. Coming to the Snake River and for many miles along, it was impossible to reach it or to get water for the oxen. We had to travel all night at times...

...On and on we journeyed—averaging 15 miles a day over cactus, sagebrush, hot sands. Everybody's shoes gave out and we bartered with Indians for mocassins, but that didn't help much about the prickly pears. One by one the oxen fell by the way...August passed. We were nearing the Cascade Mountains. The oxen were worn out, and the wagons were in poor condition to cross the mountains. Some wagons had to be left; some of the oxen were poisoned eating mountain laurel. Our provisions were exhausted by this time, and for three days we had only salal berries and some soup made by thickening water, from flour shaken from the remaining flour sack... Source: Memoirs of Harriet Palmer

1. According to the first excerpt, what were two main reasons for the westward expansion?

_____

_____

2. To what illness did Harriet's mother and many others succumb?

_____

3. What other problems are mentioned in the excerpts?

_____

_____

4. Describe the relationship with the Indians they met.

_____

_____

The Pony Express

At the start of 1860 U.S. mail between New York City and California was delivered by steamship. There were also stagecoach routes from Missouri to California. In some cases the mail took months to reach its destination, if at all. The population of California was pressuring the federal government for mail service that was more reliable and faster.

One company had the idea to hire riders to deliver mail by horseback across the almost two thousand miles of wilderness between between Missouri and California. Each rider would ride as fast as possible for about seventy-five miles day and night, beginning at his home station and stopping only for a fresh horse every ten to fifteen miles. Then a new rider would take the mail onward for the next stretch of seventy-five miles, and so on. It was like a giant relay. Many people thought it could not be done, but the government accepted the idea and issued a contract. Very soon advertisements for riders appeared in the newspapers.

Working as a Pony Express rider was difficult and dangerous, but the pay was good and it was very prestigious. Those chosen had to take an oath of allegiance to the company and had to promise that they would not swear, drink, or fight. In addition, they knew the unwritten company rule: mail, first; horse, second; self, last.

Riders were hired, horses and equipment were purchased, and stations were built and stocked. During April to June the mail left once a week from Sacramento, California, and St. Joseph, Missouri, going east and west. From mid-June to October this was increased to twice a week. It took an average of ten days in summer and twelve in winter. The route went through present-day Kansas, Nebraska, Colorado, Wyoming, Utah, Nevada, and California.

In its slightly over 18 months of existence—from April 1860 to October 1861—the Express riders covered over 650,000 miles. Only one bag of mail was not delivered. Approximately 180 men were known to have been Pony Express riders, among them Buffalo Bill Cody and Wild Bill Hickock. The youngest hired was eleven years old. As the use of the telegraph spread westward, the Pony Express was no longer needed.

The following ad for Pony Express riders was placed in a California newspaper:

WANTED
YOUNG SKINNY WIRY FELLOWS
not over eighteen. Must be expert riders willing to risk
death daily. Orphans preferred. Wages $25.00 per week.
Apply, Central Overland Express, Alta Bldg., Montgomery St.

---

1. Study the ad. What qualifications were mentioned? Evaluate each qualification. Can you think of any other desirable traits which were not mentioned?

_____

_____

_____

2. What does the ad tell you about life in the Old West?

_____

_____

_____

3. Research and report on Buffalo Bill Cody or Wild Bill Hickock.

Ten-Day Delivery!

A complete one-way delivery from St. Joseph, Missouri, to San Francisco, California, took ten days. That was about half the time taken by the Wells Fargo wagons.

Study the following ad, then answer the questions.

1. What is the purpose of the ad?

_____

_____

_____

2. What types of information are given?

_____

_____

3. How many trips were made each way each week?

_____

_____

4. When the service first began, the charge was $5.00 for the first half ounce. Why, do you think, did this change?

_____

_____

_____

5. What is the date of the ad?

_____

6. An important objective of the Pony Express was to prove the possibility of a year-round central route to the West. Before that, the only route thought feasible during certain times of the year was a southern route. Keeping in mind the date of the ad, why was finding a central route so important?

_____

_____

_____

7. Pretend it is July, 1861. Create an original recruitment ad for the Pony Express.

The ad reads:

PONY EXPRESS!

CHANGE OF TIME!   REDUCED RATES!

10 Days to San Francisco!

LETTERS

WILL BE RECEIVED AT THE

OFFICE, 84 BROADWAY,

NEW YORK,

Up to **4 P. M.** every **TUESDAY,**

AND

Up to **2½ P. M.** every **SATURDAY,**

Which will be forwarded to connect with the PONY EXPRESS leaving ST. JOSEPH, Missouri,

Every WEDNESDAY and SATURDAY at 11 P. M.

TELEGRAMS

Sent to Fort Kearney on the mornings of MONDAY and FRIDAY, will connect with **PONY** leaving St. Joseph, WEDNESDAYS and SATURDAYS.

EXPRESS CHARGES.

LETTERS weighing half ounce or under..............$1 00
For every additional half ounce or fraction of an ounce 1 00
In all cases to be enclosed in 10 cent Government Stamped Envelopes,

And all Express CHARGES Pre-paid.

PONY EXPRESS ENVELOPES For Sale at our Office.

WELLS, FARGO & CO., Ag'ts.

New York, July 1, 1861.

The Homestead Act

The Homestead Act was enacted on May 20, 1862. It provided for the distribution of public lands as a means of encouraging the Western settlement.

The following is the transcript of the first and fifth sections of the act:

Section 1. Be it enacted by the Senate and House of Representatives of the United States of America in Congress assembled, That any person who is head of a family, or who has arrived at the age of twenty-one years, and is a citizen of the United States, or who shall have filed his declaration of intention to become such, as required by the naturalization laws of the United States, and who has never borne arms against the United States Government or given aid and comfort to its enemies, shall, from and after the first of January, eighteen hundred and sixty-three, be entitled to enter one quarter section or a less quantity of unappropriated public lands, upon which said person may have filed a preemption claim, or which may at the time the application is made, be subject to preemption at one dollar and twenty-five cents, or less, per acre; or eighty acres or less of such unappropriated lands, at two dollars and fifty cents per acre, to be located in a body, in conformity to the legal subdivisions of the public lands, and after the same shall have been surveyed: Provided, That any person owning and residing on land may, under the provisions of this act, enter other land lying contiguous to his or her said land, which shall not, with the land so already owned and occupied, exceed in the aggregate one hundred and sixty acres.

Section 5. And be it further enacted, That if, at any time after the filing of the affidavit, as required in the second section of this act, and before the expiration of the five years aforesaid, it shall be proven, after due notice to the settler, to the satisfaction of the register of the land office, that the person having filed such an affidavit shall have actually changed his or her residence, or abandoned the said land for more than six months at any time, then and in that event the land so entered shall revert to the government.

1. What were the qualifications for applicants?

_____

_____

2. How much land was offered?

_____

_____

3. What promises did the applicants have to fulfill before the land became officially theirs?

_____

_____

4. What happened if an applicant failed to fulfill his residence requirement?

_____

_____

5. The South had been against the passage of an act to distribute the western lands. Why, do you suppose, did they oppose such an act?

_____

_____

6. Keeping in mind when it was passed, guess what happened to make its passage possible in spite of the southern opposition?

_____

_____

The Homestead Act

Many people took advantage of the Homestead Act as a way of owning land. The documentation on this page shows such a transaction:

Source: National Archives and Records Administration

1. Who is the new owner of the land?

_____

2. Do you recognize the owner's name?

_____

3. What do you think the letters "D. T." in the address mean?

_____

_____

4. Examine the handwriting. What does this tell you about the person?

_____

_____

_____

_____

The Transcontinental Railroad

In the early years of our nation there were several short, unconnected railroads. It was difficult, therefore, for people to travel by rail over a long distance. No private company wanted to build a railroad across the Great Plains and the Rockies because of the many dangers and obstacles. When the federal government offered to pay for the construction, two companies—the Central Pacific and the Union Pacific—decided to take the offer. Along with others, Chinese construction teams from the Central Pacific and Irish teams from the Union Pacific worked for six years against great difficulties to accomplish the job. The Chinese laborers had the complex job of laying the track across the high Sierra Mountain range. The Irish crews had to face Indian attacks and the Rocky Mountains. On May 10, 1869, the nation's first transcontinental railroad was completed at Promontory Point, Utah. The lines were joined by a spike of gold on one side and a spike of silver on the other.

The *Overland Monthly and Out West Magazine* of May 1869 described some of the problems that the construction teams of the Central Pacific faced:

> *In November following the track reached Cisco, 5,911 feet being overcome in twenty-three minutes. The summit of the Sierra was still thirteen miles off, but excepting the tunnel works, the worst part of the job on the whole line to Salt Lake was done...During the winter of 1866–67 the completion of the road to Cisco was prevented by snow, but work in the tunnels was continued, and grading on the eastern slope, beyond the snow line, was pushed with great energy...*

1. Explain the importance of the transcontinental railroad to the growth of the United States.

_____

_____

_____

_____

_____

_____

2. Research the details of the Promontory Point celebration and recreate it in your classroom.

3. With your cooperative-learning group, write a TV news report on the completion of the transcontinental railroad. Interview the dignitaries and the workers.

4. As a reporter for the *Overland Monthly and Out West Magazine,* write an account of the problems that the Union Pacific workers faced.

5. Chart the growth of railroads in this country since 1869.

6. Native Americans called a train an "Iron Horse." Evaluate that term. Although the railroad helped to connect the nation, it had a negative effect on the lives of the Native Americans. Explain.

_____

_____

_____

_____

_____

Everyday Life

In the following excerpts from her diary, Sarah Gillespie described her childhood as a pioneer farm girl in Manchester, Iowa.

January 3, 1877
It was so cold we could not go to school. Making a whip stalk. Henry, Pa, and I took some hay down to Uncle Jerome's and saw the new bridge. I got a spool of black thread for me. Henry got the papers. Mama worked on her new sofa cushion.

April 17, 1877
Go to school we had 12 scholars, the boys act real mean, the teacher said that there was not 1 boy in the whole school that tended to his own business.

1. What can you learn about everyday life from her diary entries?

_____

_____

_____

_____

2. Does anything remind you of your own life?

_____

_____

_____

3. Does anything seem really different from your own life?

_____

_____

_____

_____

4. Pretend you are a 12-year-old boy or girl living on the prairie in 1877. Write a journal entry describing a day in your life.

_____

_____

_____

_____

_____

_____

_____

_____

Unit III:

Woman Suffrage

Campaigning for Woman Suffrage in rural Nevada, July 1914
Source: Library of Congress

Woman Suffrage:
Background Information

In the early years of our nation, women had few legal rights. They could not enter into a contract, witness a document, vote in any election, or hold an office. When a woman married, her possessions became the property of her husband. The husband made all the legal decisions for the family. Few women received any type of higher education and, therefore, could not get good jobs. In the mid-seventeenth century, a few women decided to do something to remedy the situation. These dedicated people began to organize to seek ways that would win greater freedom for women. Slowly obstacles were overcome, and finally in 1920, a nineteenth amendment to the Constitution was ratified. It gave women the right to vote.

The Seneca Falls Convention—This meeting at Seneca Falls, New York, in 1848 marked the beginning of the struggle for woman suffrage. A variation of the preamble to the Declaration of Independence was presented there in a speech by Lucretia Mott.

Different Points of View on Woman Suffrage—Not all men were opposed to woman suffrage.

The Bloomer Costume—Designed by Elizabeth Smith Miller and publicized by Amelia Bloomer, this outfit became a symbol of the suffrage cause. It consisted of a knee-length dress worn over pantaloons and it allowed women more freedom in their movements.

Picketing—Acts of civil disobedience brought attention to the issue of woman suffrage. Suffragists picketed at local, county, and state offices; at polling places; at courthouses; and at other government agencies. They even picketed the White House.

The Western Vote—While still a territory, Wyoming granted voting rights to women. Other areas in the West soon followed. This gave great hope to the suffragists. They decided to concentrate their efforts in this part of the United States. Campaigning in the western states and territories was torturous work. Roads were terrible if they existed at all. Trains were often late. Settlements were distant from each other. Susan B. Anthony campaigned throughout the West for almost one continuous year.

Woman/Women—In the eighteenth and nineteenth centuries the term "woman suffrage" was used by those who worked for this cause. "Women's suffrage" was used by those who were against the suffrage movement. By the early twentieth century the concept of individual rights became more accepted. Eventually, the two terms were used interchangeably even by the suffragists.

The League of Women Voters—This voluntary public-service organization was formed in 1920 by Carrie Chapman Catt. The original purpose was to educate women about their voting rights and responsibilities. The League of Women Voters works at the local, state, and national levels to improve the entire political, economic, and social structure of our country. Men were admitted in 1974 as full members. The national headquarters is in Washington, D.C.

The Suffragettes:

Abigail Adams (1744–1818)—Because her husband was often away, Abigail Adams had much responsibility. She was an early voice for women's rights and tried to influence her husband, President John Adams, to give more legal rights and protection to women.

Susan Brownell Anthony (1820–1906)—Susan B. Anthony spent her adult life working for women's rights and suffrage. She and Elizabeth Cady Stanton were co-founders of the National Woman Suffrage Association. The two also collaborated on the first three volumes of *A History of Woman Suffrage*. Anthony wrote the fourth alone.

Carrie Chapman Catt (1859–1919)—Carrie Chapman Catt was an activist for women's rights and peace. She worked for many years as an organizer for the National American Woman Suffrage Association and became president of the organization in 1900. After the passage of the nineteenth amendment, Catt founded the League of Women Voters. After 1913, her efforts were devoted to the peace movement.

Julia Ward Howe (1819–1910)—Julia Ward Howe was an author, poet, reformer, and lecturer. She spent most of her life fighting for justice. In 1861 she wrote *The Battle Hymn of the Republic* to inspire Union soldiers to fight to end slavery.

Lucretia Mott (1793–1880)—Lucretia Mott helped found two anti-slavery organizations before helping to organize the first woman's rights convention in Seneca Falls, NY. Lucretia Mott wrote about the way women were restricted by lack of education and political rights. In 1864 she and others founded Swarthmore College in Pennsylvania.

Alice Paul (1885–1977)—Alice Paul founded the National Women's Party in 1913. She fought for the Equal Rights Amendment, which has never been ratified. She was an avid protester and was often jailed for her civil disobedience.

Anna Howard Shaw (1847–1919)—Anna Howard Shaw earned two college degrees. She was ordained in 1880 as a Methodist minister. In 1888 she met Susan B. Anthony and was soon working tirelessly with her.

Elizabeth Cady Stanton (1815–1902)—Elizabeth Cady Stanton helped to organize the first woman's rights convention. She wrote the "Declaration of Sentiments," which was modeled after the Declaration of Independence. Stanton also worked to put an end to slavery. In 1896, she and Susan B. Anthony founded the National Woman Suffrage Association.

Lucy Stone (1818–1893)—Lucy Stone worked hard to attend college and pay the fees. She was the first woman in Massachusetts to earn a college degree. Lucy Stone was an early activist for women's rights. When she married Henry Blackwell, they agreed she'd keep her own last name. She was probably the first woman to do so. Lucy Stone co-founded the American Woman Suffrage Association (AWSA).

Abigail Adams

Abigail Adams was the wife of John Adams, who became the first vice-president and the third President of the United States. John Adams was very involved with freeing America from British rule and establishing a new country. Abigail remained at home caring for their children, running the household, and managing the business of their farm and other interests. She and John wrote to each other often.

As a member of the Continental Congress and a leader in the movement for independence, John Adams was often away from his home in Braintree, Massachusetts (now Quincy). The following is an excerpt from a letter Abigail wrote to her husband on March 31, 1776:

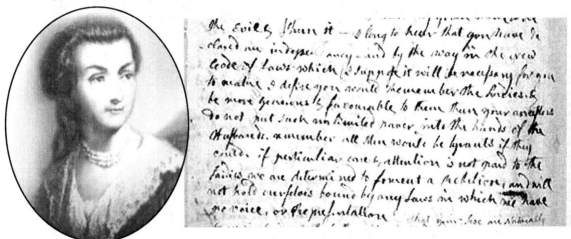

...I long to hear that you have declared an independancy—and by the way in the new Code of Laws which I suppose it will be necessary for you to make I desire you would Remember the Ladies and be more generous and favourable to them than your ancestors. Do not put such unlimited power into the hands of the Husbands. Remember all Men would be tyrants if they could. If particular care and attention is not paid to the Ladies we are determined to foment a Rebellion, and will not hold ourselves bound by any Laws in which we have no voice or Representation...

1. What is Abigail asking her husband to do?

_____

_____

2. What does Abigail predict will happen if women are not given more rights?

_____

_____

3. If you could ask Abigail one question, what would it be?

_____

4. Pretending that you are her husband, respond to this letter.

_____

_____

_____

_____

The Seneca Falls Convention

The Woman's Rights Convention at Seneca Falls, New York, marked the start of the long struggle to obtain the vote for women in the United States. Lucretia Mott, Martha Wright, Elizabeth Cady Stanton, Jane C. Hunt, and Mary Ann McClintock were the organizers of the convention. An announcement advertising the event appeared on July 14, 1848, in the *Seneca County Courier,* a small semi-weekly journal:

Woman's Rights Convention—A Convention to discuss the social, civil, and religious condition and rights of woman will be held in the Wesleyan Chapel, at Seneca Falls, N.Y., on Wednesday and Thursday, the 19th and 20th of July current; commencing at 10 o'clock a. m. During the first day the meeting will be exclusively for women, who are earnestly invited to attend. The public generally are invited to be present on the second day, when Lucretia Mott, of Philadelphia, and other ladies and gentlemen, will address the Convention.

1. Where and when was the convention to be held?

_____

_____

_____

2. Judge the decision to allow only women during the first day.

_____

_____

_____

The following is an excerpt from *The History of Woman Suffrage,* written by Susan B. Anthony, Elizabeth Cady Stanton, and Mathilda Gage.

On the first attempt to frame a resolution; to crowd a complete thought, clearly and concisely, into three lines; they felt as helpless and hopeless as if they had been suddenly asked to construct a steam engine. The ladies resigned themselves to a faithful perusal of various masculine productions.

After considering many documents, the women finally decided to base their resolution on the Declaration of Independence. *"We hold these truths to be self evident: that all men and women are created equal…"* The document also discussed the lack of women's rights and men's unreasonable authority over women. The Seneca Falls Convention inspired other women's groups all over the country to seek action in obtaining the right to vote.

1. Analyze the choice of the Declaration of Independence as their model. Judge the decision to base their resolution on this document.

_____

_____

_____

2. What important change did they make?

_____

_____

Elizabeth Cady Stanton and Susan B. Anthony

Susan B. Anthony was already working hard for abolition and temperance when she first met abolitionist and woman's rights activist Elizabeth Cady Stanton. It was the beginning of a long and close working relationship and friendship between the two. They focused their energies on woman's rights and suffrage. Although they were about the same age, they were different in many ways. Stanton was a married woman; Anthony remained single. Anthony travelled more widely in her cross-country and international speaking tours; therefore, she received more public criticism than Stanton. There were other contrasts as well.

The photograph on the left portrays Elizabeth Cady Stanton (left) and Susan B. Anthony (right).

Source: Library of Congress

The following is an excerpt from Elizabeth Cady Stanton's memoirs:

In writing we did better work together than either could do alone. While she is slow and analytical in composition, I am rapid and synthetic. I am the better writer, she the better critic. She supplied the facts and statistics, I the philosophy and rhetoric, and together we have made arguments that have stood unshaken by the storms of thirty years. Our speeches may be considered the united product of two brains.

Create a Venn diagram based on the information in the above memoir.

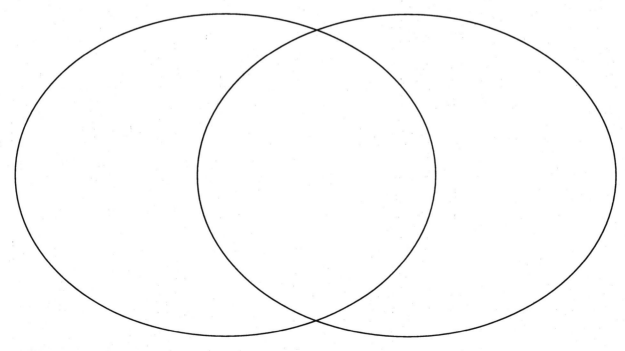

A Special Partnership

Together Elizabeth Cady Stanton and Susan B. Anthony published *The Revolution,* a radical women's rights newspaper. Along with Mathilda Gage, they also collaborated on three volumes of *A History of Woman's Suffrage.*

After the Civil War, former slaves were given the right to vote in the fourteenth and fifteenth amendments to the Constitution. Stanton and Anthony were dismayed that women were still excluded from voting, and stepped up their efforts to create awareness of the injustice. They formed the National Woman Suffrage Association and continued their joint struggle for women's rights.

When Elizabeth Cady Stanton died in 1902, Susan B. Anthony stated, "I am too crushed to speak."

Source: National Archives and Records Administration

1. Why did these two famous women work so well together?

_____

_____

_____

_____

2. Why is cooperative effort sometimes better than individual effort?

_____

_____

_____

3. Research both women. In your opinion, which woman contributed more to the cause of equal voting rights? Give your reasons.

_____

_____

_____

_____

_____

The Bloomer Costume

The 1851 Currier and Ives painting below depicts the Bloomer costume that was introduced at the Seneca Falls Woman's Convention by Elizabeth Smith Miller as a symbol of the suffrage movement. It was an alternative to the restrictive women's clothing of the times. The Bloomer costume consisted of a knee-length dress worn over full pantalettes that buttoned at the ankle. Amelia Bloomer was a feminist and editor of *The Lily,* a newspaper for women. She promoted the outfit in her writing, and it took her name. Elizabeth Smith Miller was a cousin of Suffragist Elizabeth Cady Stanton, who wore the outfit. Stanton commented about it:

I wore the dress two years and found it a blessing. What a sense of liberty I felt, in running up and down steps with my hands free to carry whatsoever, to trip through the rain or mow with no skirts to hold.

Others, especially men, ridiculed the style. The Bloomer fashion lasted until the 1880s.

THE BLOOMER COSTUME.

Source: Currier and Ives

Why did the Bloomer outfit become a symbol of the Suffrage Movement?

_____

_____

_____

_____

_____

_____

Taxation Without Representation

Lucy Stone owned a small property in New Jersey for which she was assessed property taxes. She refused to pay the taxes. In her letter to the tax collector, she explained her reasons for this refusal. As a result of this behavior, her letter was published in the *Orange Journal* and some of her personal property was sold at a tax sale.

1. What was her reason for not paying the tax?

_____

_____

_____

2. What theory of government did she rely on in her argument?

_____

_____

_____

3. What did Lucy Stone hope would result from her action?

_____

_____

_____

4. What other information can you learn from her letter?

_____

_____

_____

5. Compare the suffragettes' feelings to those of the Colonists when the Stamp Act was passed.

_____

_____

_____

_____

_____

Orange, N. J.
December 18, 1858

Mr. Mandeville, Tax Collector, Sir:

Enclosed I return my tax bill without paying it. My reason for not doing so is that women suffer taxation, and yet have no representation, which is not only unjust to one-half of the adult population, but is contrary to our theory of government. For years, some women have been paying their taxes under protest, but still taxes are imposed, and representation is not granted. The only course now left us is to refuse to pay the tax. We know what the immediate result of this refusal must be.

But we believe that when the attention of men is called to the wide difference between their theory of government and its practices, in this particular, they cannot fail to see the mistake they now make, by imposing taxes on women, while they refuse to grant them the right of suffrage, and that the sense of justice which is in all good men, will lead them to correct it. Then shall we cheerfully pay our taxes—not till then.

Respectfully,

Lucy Stone

Send a Petition

On December 26, 1865, Elizabeth Cady Stanton, Susan B. Anthony, and Lucy Stone asked their friends to send petitions to their representatives in Congress urging them to support suffrage for women. Examine the transcript of the letter that they wrote, then respond to the questions.

1. Why do you think the word Woman is capitalized?

_____

_____

_____

_____

2. Why was it so important to influence the congressmen at this time?

_____

_____

_____

_____

3. Why is there a reference to Mr. Jenckes of Rhode Island?

_____

_____

_____

_____

4. Evaluate the letter. Do you think it inspired others to write to their congressmen? Explain.

_____

_____

_____

_____

_____

_____

_____

5. Pretend that you received this letter. On another piece of paper, write a petition to send to Congress.

New York, December 26, 1865.

Dear Friend:

As the question of Suffrage is now agitating the public mind, it is the hour for Woman to make her demand.

Propositions have already been made on the floor of Congress to so amend the Constitution as to exclude Women from a voice in the Government. As this would be to turn the wheels of legislation backward, let the Women of the Nation now unitedly protest against such a desecration of the Constitution, and petition for that right which is at the foundation of all Government, the right of representation.

Send your petition, when signed, to your representative in Congress, at your earliest convenience.

Address all communications to

Standard Office, 48 Beekman St., New York.

In behalf of the National W. R. Com.

**E. CADY STANTON,
S. B. ANTHONY,
LUCY STONE.**

---

* See Bill of Mr. Jenckes, of Rhode Island.

Source: Library of Congress

African-Americans for Woman Suffrage

Many African-Americans supported the Woman Suffrage Movement. Examine this petition for Woman Suffrage, then answer the questions.

1. Who was petitioning?

_____

_____

_____

2. For what were they petitioning?

_____

_____

_____

3. Whom did they petition?

_____

_____

_____

4. Where did the petitioners reside?

_____

_____

_____

5. Who was the first to sign?

_____

PETITION FOR
WOMAN SUFFRAGE.

TO THE SENATE AND HOUSE OF REPRESENTATIVES.

Source: National Archives and Records Administration

Frederick Douglass, a former slave and well-known abolitionist, attended the convention at Seneca Falls. A week later he gave his opinion of it in the *North Star*, an antislavery newspaper he edited:

...A discussion of the rights of animals would be regarded with far more complacency by many of what are called the "wise" and the "good" of our land, than would a discussion of the rights of women...All that distinguishes man as an intelligent and accountable being, is equally true of woman, and if that government only is just which governs by the free consent of the governed, there can be no reason in the world for denying the woman the exercise of the elective franchise, or a hand in making and administering the laws of the land... The North Star, July 28, 1848

1. What is Douglass's opinion of women's rights in general and woman suffrage specifically?

_____

_____

_____

2. According to Douglass, how do many men feel about women's rights?

_____

_____

The Western Vote

Progress for suffrage was moving slowly in the East. At the same time better progress was taking place in the western United States. While not yet a state, the Territory of Wyoming granted voting rights to women in 1869. To gather even more support, Susan B. Anthony and Carrie Chapman Catt, among others, traveled throughout the West. Away from home for almost an entire year, Susan B. Anthony campaigned, gave speeches, and held rallies in Oregon, Washington, California, and Utah.

The following cartoon appeared in the *Denver Republican.* Colorado passed the referendum for woman's suffrage in 1893.

1. Is the cartoon in favor of women's suffrage? Give reasons for your answer.

_____

_____

_____

2. Who is referred to in the message at the top of the cartoon?

_____

_____

_____

3. If you could change one thing about the cartoon, what would it be?

_____

_____

_____

_____

A Cartoonist's Look at Woman's Rights

In 1869, this cartoon was published by Currier and Ives. At the time, opposition to woman suffrage remained strong. Even well-known figures like Horace Greeley expressed disfavor:

As to woman's voting, our judgement does not favor it—because it would double the cost and trouble of elections to no purpose.

Analyze the Currier and Ives cartoon below.

THE AGE OF BRASS.
or the triumphs of Woman's rights

1. How are the women in the cartoon characterized? Give specific examples.

_____

_____

_____

_____

2. Evaluate the sarcasm in the statement written on the center sign. To whom does it refer?

_____

_____

_____

3. How is the man in the picture depicted?

_____

_____

4. What is the point of view of the cartoonist?

_____

_____

Susan B. Anthony Votes

In 1872 Susan B. Anthony and thirteen others convinced the registrars to accept their ballots. Only Susan B. Anthony was later charged with breaking the law.

...[She did] knowingly, wrongfully, and unlawfully vote...without having a lawful right to vote...(the said Susan B. Anthony being then and there a person of the female sex,)...

UNITED STATES

CIRCUIT COURT.

Northern District of New York.

THE UNITED STATES OF AMERICA
vs.
SUSAN B. ANTHONY.

Hon. WARD HUNT, Presiding.

APPEARANCES.
For the United States:
HON. RICHARD CROWLEY.
U. S. District Attorney.

For the Defendant:
HON. HENRY R. SELDEN.
JOHN VAN VOORHIS, ESQ.

Tried at Canandaigua. Tuesday and Wednesday, June 17th and 18th, 1873. before Hon. Ward Hunt, and a jury.

1. What is the reason for the document?

_____

_____

_____

2. Who was the judge?

_____

3. Who was the prosecutor?

_____

4. Who defended Ms. Anthony?

_____

5. Where did the trial take place?

_____

6. Do you think the women broke the law?

_____

7. Why, do you think, was Ms. Anthony the only one charged?

_____

The judge never let the case go to the jury. Instead, he read the following statement before the final arguments were made. He also denied all requests for an appeal.

I have decided as a question of law...that under the Fourteenth Amendment, which Miss Anthony claims protects her, she was not protected in a right to vote...I therefore direct that you find a verdict of guilty.

1. Research and find out what was unusual about the judge.

_____

_____

2. Read the fourteenth amendment. Do you agree with the judge?

_____

_____

3. Evaluate the judge's handling of the case.

_____

_____

"The Apotheosis of Suffrage"

The following drawing, "The Apotheosis of Suffrage," was created by George Yost Coffin. It was published in the *Washington Post* on January 26, 1896.

Source: Library of Congress

"The Apotheosis of Suffrage"

1. What is the meaning of *apotheosis?*

_____

_____

2. What women are included? How are they depicted?

_____

_____

3. How is symbolism used in this cartoon?

_____

_____

4. What information is supplied in the document?

_____

_____

5. How do you interpret the presence of George Washington?

_____

_____

6. Compare and contrast this cartoon with the one on page 70.

_____

_____

_____

Alice Paul

Alice Paul is remembered as a feminist, suffragist, and political activist. She was born on January 11, 1885, near Moorestown, New Jersey. Her parents were Quakers, and Alice was raised with the belief that men and women had equal rights. Among her achievements were the National Woman's Party, which she founded in 1913; the inclusion of gender equality in the United Nations Charter; and the design of the Equal Rights Amendment in 1923. Alice was an activist and organized pro-suffrage demonstrations, which sometimes ended in a jail sentence for her. Alice Paul died on July 9, 1977, without seeing the Equal Rights Amendment passed. Her legacy lives on to inspire others to continue the fight for social justice for all.

The woman described in the following poem is Alice Paul.

I watched a river of women,
Rippling purple, white, and golden,
Stream toward the National Capitol.

Along its border,
Like a purple flower floating,
Moved a young woman, worn, wraithlike,
With eyes alight, keenly observing the marchers.
Out there on the curb, she looked so little, so lonely;
Few appeared even to see her;
No one saluted her.

Yet commander was she of the column, its leader;
She was the spring whence arose that irresistible river of women
Streaming steadily towards the National Capitol.
   Katherine Rolston Fisher
   The Suffragist, January 19, 1918
Source: *The Story of Alice Paul,* by Inez Hayes Irwin, Denlinger's Publishers, Fairfax, VA

1. Read the poem above. Write two facts that you have learned about the Woman's Suffrage Movement or Alice Paul from reading the poem.

_____

_____

_____

2. What is the mood of the poem?

_____

_____

3. Rewrite the poem into a news article that describes the demonstration.

4. Illustrate the poem. What images do the words inspire?

5. Do you think that the Equal Rights Amendment will ever be passed? Explain your reasons.

_____

_____

_____

Letters from a Suffragette: Alice Paul

Alice Paul attended the London School of Economics in 1909. It was during this time that she became involved in the movement to obtain the voting right for women. In England, as in America, only men had the right to vote. Alice joined the Women's Social and Political Union in London and began working for the cause. Although full of enthusiasm, Alice experienced some hardships. She described them in letters sent to her mother in New Jersey. The following are transcripts of some of those letters.

March 17, 1909

Dear Momma,

On Tuesday I went on deputation of the suffragettes to the House of Commons and 108 of us were arrested and also 8 men who tried to help us. About 200 of us started out. It was very exciting. We went out at 8 P.M., and the next day we were to be tried at the Police Court. The judge adjourned the trial till July so that they might investigate a point made by the defence that will prove that Mr. Asquith (Prime Minister) took illegal action, not us. We are now out on bail.

December 10, 1909

Dear Momma,

I came out of prison at 8 o'clock yesterday morning. I got thy letters there. I am sorry that thee was so worried. I thought that thee might be, so I decided to not let thee know I had gone until I came out.

December 20, 1909

Dear Momma,

I will now tell what forcible feeding is like. We took no food when we went to prison and they let us starve till the third day. On the morning of the third day, the warden came in and dragged me out into the next cell and put me in a chair. Then the doctor fed me by a tube which is about 5 or 6 feet long inserted through the nose and down into the stomach. When it was over, I was in shock and felt sick to my stomach. My nose bled for 10 minutes. They carried me back and wrapped me up. In the evening, the same process was repeated, this time I was tied to a chair.

Courtesy Alice Paul Society, Moorestown, NJ

1. What have you learned about the life of a suffragette from reading Alice's letters?

_____

_____

_____

2. Which words point out Alice's Quaker roots?

_____

_____

3. What character traits did Alice possess?

_____

_____

4. Evaluate Alice's punishment for picketing and being considered a "public nuisance." Was it too harsh, or did the punishment fit the crime?

_____

_____

Parading for Suffrage

Many parades were held to garner support for woman's suffrage. The marchers obtained the necessary parade permits before taking to the streets. Often the marchers were met with jeering crowds. At times they were spat at and had objects thrown at them. There were occasions when they were attacked by mobs.

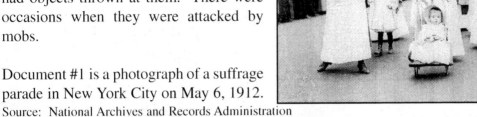

Document #1 is a photograph of a suffrage parade in New York City on May 6, 1912.
Source: National Archives and Records Administration

Document #2 is the program cover from another parade. Printed in full color, the marcher behind the horse is wearing a white dress with a red, white, and blue ribbon. The horse is white. The banner from the trumpet reads, "Votes for Women."
Courtesy Lyndon B. Johnson Library, Austin, Texas

1. What symbols are used in the program cover?

_____

_____

_____

2. What types of messages are used: visual, verbal, or both?

_____

_____

_____

3. What is the main idea expressed by the artwork?

_____

_____

_____

4. Describe one of the parades from the point of view of one of the marchers.

_____

_____

_____

Picketing the White House

An amendment for woman's suffrage was introduced in Congress in 1878. Suffragists worked in many ways to bring pressure on politicians. President Wilson was openly opposed to this amendment. In 1917 and 1918 women picketed the White House. They marched outside the grounds for six months. The women were heckled and many were arrested. The photographs below show some of these women during the picketing campaign.

Photo #1: November 19, 1918

1. What is meant by calling the President "Kaiser Wilson?"

_____

_____

_____

2. What information is given in the photograph?

_____

_____

_____

Source: National Archives and Records Administration

Source: National Women's Party Collection

Photo #2: College Day in the Picket Line, February 1917

1. What questions are asked of the President?

_____

_____

2. What in the picture tells you the women are serious about what they are doing?

_____

_____

3. What is the importance of these photographs?

_____

_____

_____

Why Women Should Vote

In the early twentieth century, there were some men who urged some support for women's suffrage in the United States. Among them was Arthur Brisbane, a writer for the Hearst Newspapers. The following excerpts are from an article written by Brisbane in 1917:

In this country and throughout the world, women progress toward the full possession of the ballot and toward equality with men in educational facilities. The woman who votes becomes an important factor in life. In the first place, when a woman votes, the candidate must take care that his conduct and record meet with a good woman's approval, and this makes better men of the candidates. Men can deceive each other more easily than they can deceive women. Our social system improves in proportion as the men in it are influenced by its good women.

The education of a girl is important chiefly because it means the education of a future mother. Whose brain but the mother's inspires and directs the son in the early years, when knowledge is most easily absorbed and permanently retained? Well educated women are essential to society. Voting by women will improve humanity.

1. Compare and contrast Brisbane's thoughts about women in 1917 with the way that women are regarded today. What has changed? What remains the same?

_____

_____

_____

_____

_____

2. Do you agree or disagree that "men can deceive each other more easily than they can deceive women?" Explain.

_____

_____

_____

_____

3. Examine the photograph on the right. Look at the faces of the onlookers and determine which ones might have supported woman suffrage and which ones were opposed to it.

Source: Library of Congress

Campaigning for Suffrage

Many different activities were organized to gather support for woman suffrage. Parades, picketing, speeches, petitions, and rallies were held for many years. The following document describes a different type of activity. Examine the document to answer these questions.

1. What type of document is it?

_____

_____

2. What is the purpose of the document?

_____

_____

3. Who sponsored the event?

_____

_____

_____

4. List three things the author said which you think are important.

_____

_____

_____

_____

_____

_____

5. What two things does the document tell you about life in the United States at this time?

_____

_____

_____

_____

_____

Women's Political Union of New Jersey
HEADQUARTERS: 79 HALSEY STREET, NEWARK, N. J.
TELEPHONE 3150 MULBERRY

OFFICERS
President: MRS. MINA C. VAN WINKLE, Newark

SUFFRAGE BASE BALL GAME
KANSAS CITY vs. NEWARK
Ladies' Day--Friday, June 25, 1915--2:30 P. M.

Dear Fellow Suffragist:--

Herewith inclosed are five tickets which we ask you to kindly distribute among men who are sure to use them. Free admission to women.

We make a profit of 10 cents and 25 cents on each ticket sold. Please help us earn money for our campaign!

An auto parade with decorated cars will proceed to the grounds from our headquarters. Notable suffrage speakers will address the men on the bleachers and the grand stands. Our women will sell all kinds of supplies.

The attendance at a big game of this kind is usually ten thousand, and has been as high as thirty thousand. This is our biggest opportunity of the year. You are urged to help us make a creditable demonstration.

MRS. FRANK H. SOMMER, Chairman.

Source: Women's Political Union Collection, New Jersey Historical Society

The Nineteenth Amendment

The amendment that guarantees women in America the right to vote is shown below. This is a copy of the joint resolution of the sixty-sixth Congress; it proposed the nineteenth amendment to the Constitution. The amendment was ratified by two-thirds of the states and finally signed into law on August 26, 1920. None of the leaders of the woman suffrage movement were invited to witness the signing, and no photos were taken. Susan B. Anthony died fourteen years before the nineteenth amendment was added to the Constitution.

Sixty-sixth Congress of the United States of America;

At the First Session,

Begun and held at the City of Washington on Monday, the nineteenth day of May, one thousand nine hundred and nineteen.

JOINT RESOLUTION

Proposing an amendment to the Constitution extending the right of suffrage to women.

Resolved by the Senate and House of Representatives of the United States of America in Congress assembled (two-thirds of each House concurring therein), That the following article is proposed as an amendment to the Constitution, which shall be valid to all intents and purposes as part of the Constitution when ratified by the legislatures of three-fourths of the several States.

"ARTICLE ————.

"The right of citizens of the United States to vote shall not be denied or abridged by the United States or by any State on account of sex.

"Congress shall have power to enforce this article by appropriate legislation."

F. H. Gillett
Speaker of the House of Representatives.

Thos. R. Marshall.
Vice President of the United States and
President of the Senate.

Examine the resolution document.

1. What is the date of the resolution?

_____

2. How long did it take to get the amendment ratified?

_____

3. What portion of each state legislature was needed to pass the new law?

_____

4. Divide into groups and research the campaign for ratification of the amendment. Which state was the first to ratify? Which was last? Which states did not ratify? Was it difficult to achieve ratification? Explain.

_____
_____
_____
_____
_____

_____
_____
_____
_____
_____
_____

5. Why, do you think, were no women invited to the signing ceremony?

_____
_____
_____

ANSWERS

The American Revolution
Page 11
1. Since this was a British cartoon, the point of view of the artist supports England. It emphasizes the violent behavior of the colonists toward British law. The tea tax collector in the cartoon has met with harsh treatment from the Patriots.
2. In the background, men who are thinly disguised as Indians are dumping chests of tea into Boston Harbor.
3. The word TEA is printed on the pot that the Patriot is holding as he pours tea into the throat of the tax collector, or "Exciseman." This symbolizes the resistance to the Tea Act by the colonists.
4. The tax collector has been tarred and feathered by the Sons of Liberty and also humiliated.

Page 13
1. The Stamp Act document was written in England.
2. The act took effect on March 22, 1765.
3. The idea that "defraying the expenses" was necessary was repeated: "towards further defraying the expenses of defending, protecting, and securing the same" [British colonies and plantations in America]; "appropriated toward defraying the expenses of defending, protecting, and securing the British colonies and plantations in America"; and "raising further revenue toward…defraying the said expenses."
4. Patrick Henry introduced a set of resolves that denounced the power of England to tax the colonies unfairly. In his speech he said, "Caesar had his Brutus, Charles the First his Cromwell, and George III—may he profit from their example."
5. Vocabulary:
   demurrer: objector
   pence: plural of penny (British)
   rejoinder: response
   revenue: money from taxes
   vellum: parchment
6. Answers will vary.

Page 14
1. Paul Revere was the engraver.
2. In the engraving, the British grenadiers are standing in a straight line and shooting their rifles at the inhabitants of the city. Opinions may vary to whether it is realistic or not. Students may point out the following in the photo: Some men are lying on the ground; other people are watching in horror; a small dog is observing the action; none of the inhabitants has a weapon; the massacre is taking place on a city street.
3. Opinions may vary.
4. Captain Thomas Preston of the British Army and eight soldiers were indicted for the murder of Crispus Attucks and other citizens. Preston and six of the soldiers were acquitted of the crimes. Two of the soldiers were convicted of manslaughter. Opinions may vary on the justice of the trial.

Page 15
1. This notice was a call to action for the Patriots to meet at the Liberty Tree.
2. The notice contains the time of the meeting (12 noon) the location of the meeting (Liberty Tree) and information about the purpose of the meeting.
3. The author hopes that at the Liberty Tree meeting, all people who ordered the teas will resign from office and swear in public to return the teas to England.
4. The Patriot group that posted the notice strongly warns against taking the notice down.
5. Opinions will vary.

Page 16
1. Dr. Warren asked Paul Revere to ride to Lexington and warn John Hancock and Samuel Adams that they were in danger of being arrested for treason by British General Gage.
2. Revere needed a good horse because it was a long ride and a very important task.
3. The mission was successful. Revere alerted the captain of the Minute-Men and people in almost every house along the way. The men were not arrested.
4. Comparisons will vary. The signals "one if by land, and two if by sea," are mentioned in the poem but not the letter.

Page 17
1. Opinions will vary, but Henry's fiery speech influenced others to take up the cause of liberty from England.
2. Other speeches that have had great influence include Lincoln's *Gettysburg Address* and Martin Luther King Jr.'s *I Have a Dream* speech.
3. Vocabulary:
   extenuate: to make the seriousness of guilt, fault, offense, etc. seem less
   idle: not busy; doing nothing
   brethren: fellow members of a church, group, or society
   clash: loud sound
   gale: storm
   endowed: provided with money, property, gift
   unalienable: cannot be given or taken away

Page 18
1. Franklin wrote to the British Governor of Massachusetts explaining that the colonists would deeply resent not having a voice in important matters such as taxation.
2. Franklin feared "everything would go into confusion" and feuds would arise, perhaps leading to serious conflict.
3. The letter was a serious warning of things to come. The British did not heed the warning.

Page 19
Top
1. *Common Sense* was published in Philadelphia in 1776. It was addressed to the general population of Americans.
2. Subjects contained in *Common Sense* included the origin and design of the government, monarchy and heredity succession issues, thoughts on the state of American affairs, discussion of the present ability of America to engage in war and miscellaneous reflections from the author.
Bottom
1. The author's purpose in writing *The Crisis* was to state his belief that Americans should stand up to the tyranny of England in a bold way.
2. Opinions will vary, but it is short, succinct, alliterative, and to the point.
3. The summer soldier and the sunshine patriot are examples of people who were half-hearted about the problems caused by England. They were not willing to give all their support to the cause.
4. General Washington used this essay with his troops to motivate and inspire them in battle.

Page 20
Top
1. Opinions will vary, but the skills include his skill and experience as an officer, his independent fortune, his good character and his ability to unite.
2. John Hancock was surprised and disappointed with the choice of Washington. He had expected the commission himself.
Bottom
1. The recipient was the president of the Continental Congress, John Hancock. Hancock served as president from May 24, 1775 to Oct. 29, 1777. George Washington read the letter in person to the Continental Congress.
2. George Washington wondered if he were up to the task of being commander-in-chief. He worried that he was not experienced enough.
3. Because Washington felt that it was the wish of Congress to appoint him as the leader of the Continental Army, he was willing to take on the responsibility.
4. Washington requested no payment for the job; he just wanted to be repaid for his expenses. He promised to keep an account of his expenses.
5. Opinions will vary.

Page 21
1. Washington probably capitalized UNITED PROVINCES in his speech to show that all colonies should now be unified in their support for the troops and their cause.
2. Opinions will vary.

Page 23

1. The purpose of this important document was to sever political ties with England and become an independent nation with its own government.
2. The document is addressed to King George III of England.
3. Answers may vary, but may include the following: The King refused to agree to laws that the colonists needed. The King blocked the justice system by refusing to give proper power to the judges and courts. The King kept a standing army in the colonies in times of peace without consent of the colonial governments.
4. Answers will vary, but John Hancock, Benjamin Franklin, and Richard Stockton are three famous ones.
5. Answers will vary.
6. John Hancock was the first to sign and wrote his name large and black. He said, "King George can read that without his spectacles."
7. It is kept in the National Archives Building in Washington, D.C.

Page 24

1. Opinions will vary.
2. The letters on the Join or Die cartoon represent the colonies.
3. In addition to the rattlesnake, a griffin is included on the masthead.
4. Information on the masthead includes the date, the name of the newspaper, and the volume of the edition.
5. In the Join or Die editorial cartoon, the rattlesnake is in segments, similar to the separation of the colonies. In the second example, the Don't Tread On Me flag, the snake is shown whole. In the Gadsden version of the flag, the snake is coiled. On the bottom of the page, in the masthead example, the rattlesnake is depicted as whole and in contact with the griffin.

Page 25

1. The British used the lyrics of the song to mock the American soldiers. The word "Yankee" refers to New Englanders, and the word "Doodle" means foolish. The British thought the American soldiers were unsophisticated in the way they dressed. A soldier could just "stick a feather in his hat" and call it "Macaroni." Macaroni was a style of wig that was very fashionable in England.
2. Hasty pudding was originally British, but was adopted by the colonists. It is a pudding or porridge made from grains, or cornmeal and cooked in milk or water. Maple syrup or brown sugar can be added. It was called hasty pudding, because it could be made in a short time.
3. This activity will vary.

Page 26

1. Washington's orders included the following: All boats or water craft were to be secured or destroyed. Boats kept at Tinicum were gathered to be used for transportation of the troops and, therefore, had to be guarded carefully. Boats at other locations could be brought to Tinicum or destroyed so the enemy could not take them and use them to cross the Delaware River.
2. Opinions will vary.
3. Opinions will vary, but Washington was a thoughtful, clever, determined leader.
4. In the letter, General Washington advised General Maxwell to secure or destroy all the water craft on the Pennsylvania side of the river so that the enemy would not be able to use them. This proved to be an excellent strategy. British General Howe could not find boats to use for his men to cross the river. The Americans defeated the Hessian soldiers in Trenton.

Page 27

1. To try to help his suffering soldiers, Washington wrote a letter to Governor George Clinton detailing the difficult situation and asking for help. He wrote with compassion when he described the soldiers as naked and starving and remarked that only the most active efforts might avert a catastrophe at Valley Forge.
2. Washington stated, " We cannot enough admire the incomparable patience and fidelity of the soldiers." He was very proud of them.

Page 28

1. The generals were Major General Charles Lee, Marquis de Lafayette, General Wayne, General Scott, General Stirling, and General Greene.
2. Information shown on the map includes troop positions, distances, and locations.
3. Opinions will vary, but it boosted American morale and lowered the British morale. It gave Americans hope of gaining their independence from Britain.

Page 29

1. Opinions will vary.
2. The ships appear to be very close to each other, and in fact, were locked together by grappling hooks during the battle. Also observed in the photo are explosions and gunfire. It was a fierce battle.
3. John Paul Jones received the nickname "Father of the Navy" because he was courageous in battle and captured the tenacious spirit of the nation's early navy when he said, "I have not yet begun to fight."

Page 30

1. The sailor managed to climb onto the ship and set off a hand grenade in an attempt to destroy the *Serapis,* although it meant his certain death.
2. The sailor refers to opening the hatch and looking down the hold on the ship when he says, "the yawning throat." "The devil's pill" is the hand grenade.
3. The poet probably wrote the poem as a centennial tribute to one of the bloodiest battles in US naval history.

Page 31

1. Vocabulary:
   parapet: a low wall or mound of stones that protects soldiers
   parley: to discuss matters or settle disputes, especially with an enemy
2. Answers will vary.
3. Answers will vary.

Page 32

1. In the painting, both sides display flags. However, while the Americans proudly fly the American flag, the British flag that is portrayed is white and indicates surrender.
2. Opinions will vary.
3. In the song, the lyrics describe things that are turned upside down. Britain's idea of a conclusion to the war had been turned upside down. Its strong and experienced army suffered defeat from a fledgling American army and was forced to surrender and give America its independence.

Page 34

1. The treaty was generous to America in that the King of England finally acknowledged the freedom, sovereignty, and independence of the colonies, and he relinquished all future claim to them. The treaty was generous to America in a number of other ways as well (in other Articles). The territory of the United States was to include land from the Atlantic coast to the Mississippi River and from Florida to Canada. Britain released all claims to territorial rights, giving up the whole Northwest territory. American fishermen's rights to fish off Newfoundland and in the Gulf of St. Lawrence would continue.
2. The most important part of Article I was "His Britannic Majesty acknowledges the United States to be free, sovereign, and independent." America had won its independence from Britain. Article VII speaks of prisoner exchanges, all property (including slaves) would remain with the owners, and the withdrawal of all British forces from America.

Westward Expansion
Page 39

1. Answers will vary.
2. Plenipotentiary: invested with full power
3. Rights given to America include all the adjacent islands of the territory, public buildings, parks, and military forts. The inhabitants of the territory shall become U.S. Citizens as soon as possible. They will be maintained and protected. The U.S. must respect the treaties made between the "tribes" and the former governments. Rights given to France include the following: troops will be allowed to leave within 3 months; French and Spanish merchant ships will have access to the port of New Orleans for 12 years; merchant ships of France shall have "most favored nation" status following the 12th year; and all documents and archives will remain the property of the French government.
4. Answers will vary. Perhaps the tone of the treaty is formal, yet fair.
5. Results may vary depending partly on teacher instructions.

Page 40

1. The rights being protected are the free enjoyment of life, liberty, property and religion.
2. The military, civil, and judicial powers in place will continue their responsibilities.
3. Answers will vary.

Page 41

1. The dates indicate the starting and ending dates of a portion of their trip.
2. When compared with a current U.S. map you will see that parts of Oregon, Washington and Idaho are shown on the map of Lewis and Clark.
3. The routes crossed mountains, followed rivers, crossed rivers and crossed the Continental Divide.
4. At the time, this map was important because it showed others the location of mountain ranges and passes, rivers and portages, possible routes, the routes used and existing settlements (Lewiston).

Page 42

1. The date of the document is November 7, 1805.
2. The Pacific Ocean was their final goal. Perhaps he heard a river running or a waterfall.
3. He is happy and excited. He seems to express a feeling of relief.
4. A rocky shore is mentioned.
5. Some accounts say eighteen months. Others count the beginning of the trip at Ft. DuBois (Indiana) and say 13 months.
6. This journey allowed our government to learn about natural resources, animal and plant life, and future transportation possibilities. Our government also learned the value of the purchase of this territory.

Page 43

1. The ad was place by Ashley and Henry.
2. This is a help-wanted ad for hunters and trappers.
3. They will hire one hundred men. The pay will be $200 per year. They will leave on or before March 1. Applicants are asked to see W. Ashley or J. V. Garnier.
4. By the nature of their travels, the trappers will gather information about the territory. Eventually others will follow in their footsteps and establish trading posts, settlements, etc.
5. There was probably a demand for fur. The furriers and trappers were among the first to head west.

Page 44

Answers will vary.

Page 45

1. President Jackson's remarks seem cold and uncaring. No, the move was not a good one for the Cherokee. They lost their homes, real estate, possessions and structure of their community. Also, many died along the way.
2. John Ross, an educated and wealthy man, was 1/8 Cherokee and served as their only elected chief. He fought for their rights in the newspapers and the courts. Davy Crockett was a Congressman; he argued for the rights of the Cherokee. He did everything he could to help them.
3. It seems that Burnett did not agree with the forced removal and felt sympathy for these people. He did as ordered, but he was saddened by what was being done.
4. Answers will vary.
5. Answers will vary.

Page 46

1. Answers will vary.
2. New Helvetica was the name of a farming colony that Johann Sutter had established.
3. Answers will vary.
4. John Marshall was the man who built the sawmill for Johann Sutter at his New Helvetica settlement.

Page 47

1. Answers will vary, but the following gold-mining tools are possibilities;
A gold pan is used device for washing small samples.
A cradle, or rocker box, is used by two to four men teams. The box is placed near a stream or river bank. Pay dirt is shoveled into a tray with a **screen (sieve)**. Water is then added and the box is rocked to help the water wash through the dirt, separating the gold from the rest of the material.
A long tom is a wooden box about 12 to 15 feet long. It works in mush the same way as a rocker box.
2. A cradle rocked back and forth, separating the gold and allowing the sediment to wash away. A long tom was a wooden chute through which water flowed. As it flowed, the stones and other sediment were separated by the running water and a series of ruffles. Both the cradle and long Tom were used when a there was a known deposit of gold.

Page 48

Top

1. They crossed the Missouri River on a big flatboat (barge or raft).
2. People discarded unnecessary items as they traveled to lighten the load they or their animals carried.
3. Answers will vary.
4. Answers will vary.
5. Answers will vary.

Bottom

1. He was caught up in the excitement of "gold fever."
2. There were new gold discoveries on the Frazier River.
3. They were waiting for "the river to fall."
4. Answers will vary.

Page 49

1. Answers will vary.
2. The oxen look like they are working hard. The animals look tired.
3. Six wagons can be seen. There are probably many more.
4. It looks like women and children are riding in the wagon.
5. There may not be room in the wagon for everyone to ride at once. They may want some exercise and a change from riding in a bumpy wagon. They may want to lighten the load of the wagon.
6. Answers will vary.

Page 50

1. The two reasons mentioned were the discovery of gold and the fertile farm lands.
2. Her mother died of cholera.
3. Their shoes wore out, the animals got tired and weak; the wagons were in poor condition; and there was a lack of food.
4. It is mentioned that they traded with Indians for moccasins.

Page 51

1. The applicants should be no older than eighteen years old, have wiry builds, be expert riders, and be willing to risk death. It was also preferred that they were orphans. Answers will vary as to the other traits necessary.
2. It was a dangerous time. Also, there were many who were "on their own" at an early age.
3. Answers will vary.

Page 52

1. The ad tells others about the service they provide.
2. The ad tells the price, how long delivery takes, and where and when to deliver the messages.
3. Trips were made twice a week.
4. Answers will vary.
5. The ad is dated July 1, 1861.
6. Answers may vary, but remember the political scene at the time. The date of the ad indicates that the Civil War has begun. Communication with the western territories and states would be very important.
7. Answers will vary.

Page 53

1. Applicants must be at least twenty-one years of age, a U.S. citizen (or officially filed to become a citizen), be the head of the household, and never have "borne arms against the U.S."
2. One quarter section or less was offered.
3. They had to live on the land for five years and could not leave the land for a period of more than six months.
4. The land became the property of the government again.
5. Answers will vary, but the Southern states feared that more states would be formed and that they would be anti-slavery.
6. Answers will vary, but with the formation of the Confederate States of America, the southern states no longer had a vote in the U.S. Congress and, therefore, their opposition did not matter.

Page 54

1. The deed to the land was held by Charles P. Ingalls.
2. Charles P. Ingalls was father of Laura Ingalls Wilder, author of the Little House on the Prairie books.

3. Answers may vary, but it stands for Dakota Territory.
4. The person has had some education.

Page 55

1. The transcontinental rail system made it easier to move products and people from one part of the United States to another. It made long-distance travel of people and mail faster and easier.
2. Answers will vary.
3. Answers will vary.
4. Answers will vary.
5. Railroads grew quickly until about the 1960s.
6. Answers will vary. "Iron horse" a metaphor. The locomotive took the place of the horse. The railroads brought quick development and rapid growth of new settlements on lands previously used by the native tribes.

Page 56

1. A new bridge was an exciting occurrence. Not much exciting happened; it was worth mentioning that she got a spool of thread. Their everyday life was very simple.
2. Answers will vary.
3. Answers will vary.
4. Answers will vary.

Woman Suffrage

Page 61

1. Abigail Adams requests that women be given more rights. She states that women have no voice or representation in determining laws. She worries that unlimited power might be given to husbands "who could be tyrants."
2. If women are not given more rights, Abigail says that they will start a rebellion.
3. Answers will vary.
4. Answers will vary.

Page 62

Top
1. The convention was to be held in the Wesleyan Chapel at Seneca Falls, New York. The time of the meeting was 10 a.m. on July 19 and 20, 1848.
2. Opinions will vary.
Bottom
1. The women chose to model their document after the Declaration of Independence. The format of the Declaration of Independence allowed them to organize their points and petition for rights. The women listed 18 injuries and usurpations that men used against women—the same number of charges that the Patriots had listed against the King of England in the Declaration of Independence. Opinions will vary as to the decision to use the Declaration of Independence as a guide.
2. The women's said "all men and WOMEN are created equal." The Declaration of Independence only mentioned men.

Page 63

Elizabeth Cady Stanton	**Both**	**Susan B. Anthony**
rapid and synthetic in writing	worked better together	better critic
better writer	speeches were created together	slow and analytic
supplied philosophy & rhetoric	long friendship	supplied facts and statistics

Page 64

1. Susan B. Anthony and Elizabeth Cady Stanton had common goals. They both strongly believed in women's rights and fought a joint struggle against injustice toward women.
2. Opinions will vary.
3. Opinions will vary.

Page 65

Women who wore the Bloomer costume were very involved with dress reform and the women's movement. These women felt that the bloomer outfit was more practical to wear. In the era of the 1850s, most women wore full skirts with lots of petticoats, and these outfits often hindered full participation in activities. The Bloomer fashion became a symbol of women's independence.

Page 66

1. She did not think it was fair to tax women if they had no representation.
2. She relied on the theory that our government was based on "no taxation without representation."
3. Lucy Stone hoped that men would see the injustice of this practice and grant women the right to vote.
4. The letter was written on December 18, 1858, from Orange, NJ. Mr. Mandeville was the tax collector.
5. Answers will vary. The colonists' feelings that they should not pay taxes to England without the right of representation was very similar to the suffragists' feelings.

Page 67

1. Answers may vary, but perhaps it was capitalized to lend emphasis and importance.
2. It was important because Congress was about to vote on legislation making it even more difficult for women to vote.
3. Mr. Jenckes was a Congressman representing Rhode Island.
4. Answers will vary.
5. Answers will vary.

Page 68

Top
1. African Americans who supported the Suffrage Movement signed the petition. Frederick Douglass signed at the top.
2. They were petitioning for women to have the right to vote.
3. The petition was sent to the U.S. Senate and the House of Representatives.
4. They resided in Washington, D.C.
5. Frederick Douglas Jr. was first to sign.

Bottom
1. He believed that women are as intelligent and accountable as men and that they should not be denied the right to vote.
2. He thought that many men were more concerned with animals' rights than with women's rights.

Page 69

1. The cartoon favors women having the right to vote. The men seem uncertain about giving them this right. The women are looking to the men for justice. The way they are lined up on either side seems to infer that women are equal to men.
2. The message refers to women. It says that men should keep them in mind when voting.
3. Answers will vary.

Page 70

1. One woman is shown as bossing a man who is holding an infant. One is dressed as Uncle Sam and seems very political. She appears to be signing a petition, possibly stirring up trouble. Another is immodestly showing her legs.
2. It refers to Susan B. Anthony, calling her a "man tamer."
3. The man appears to be afraid of the woman.
4. The artist is anti-suffrage.

Page 71

Top
1. This document shows details of the trial of Susan B. Anthony in which she was charged with illegal voting.
2. The judge was the Honorable Ward Hunt.
3. The district attorney representing the government was Richard Crowley.
4. Henry R. Seldon and John Van Voorhis represented Miss Anthony.
5. The trial took place in Canandaigua, New York.
6. Answers will vary, but Miss Anthony and the others were permitted to cast their ballots by the registrars.
7. Answers may vary, but they probably wanted to make an example of her to deter others from doing what she did.

Bottom
1. Answers will vary, but the following are interesting facts: The judge found Anthony guilty without allowing the jurors to deliberate and without polling them. It was unusual for the judge to issue the verdict rather than let the jury deliberate. In 1895 the Supreme Court ruled that a federal judge could not direct a guilty verdict in a criminal trial. Also, in 1878, Hunt suffered a paralyzing stroke. He could not attend court sessions or render opinions but did not retire so he could continue to get his pension. Congress passed a special provision under which he could receive a pension if he would retire within 30 days, which he did.

2. Answers will vary.

3. Answers will vary.

Page 72

1. *Apotheosis* means elevating to the level of a god.

2. To the left of George Washington is Elizabeth Cady Stanton. On his right is Susan B. Anthony.

3. This cartoon seems to mock the movement. Stanton is holding a weapon and Anthony is making a lot of noise with her horn. George Washington in a skirt appears to be "one of the girls." The trumpet might represent the "noise" being made by these women. The weapon might symbolize the fight these women are waging for the right to vote. The bible held by Stanton gives the idea that suffrage is being elevated to a divine status.

4. It shows that it is the twenty-eighth annual convention.

5. Answers will vary, but showing Washington in a skirt may infer that the women think they are as important as he.

6. Answers will vary. Both the Age of Brass cartoon and the Apotheosis of Suffrage cartoon mock the suffrage movement. The Age of Brass cartoon may be more direct in its objective. It is from the point of view of a male artist as to how suffrage would change the everyday lives of men. In the view of the artist, women would "take over." Women are shown as breaking with traditions (e.g., smoking, voting, showing legs). The Apotheosis cartoon is a little more subtle. The Apotheosis depicts real people. The Age of Brass cartoon does not. George Washington appears in the Apotheosis cartoon.

Page 73

1. We learn that the women marched toward the National Capitol. The poet tells us that Alice Paul was the organizer of this particular parade. She was the inspiration for the women in the march.

2. Answers will vary, but possibilities are *serious, hopeful* and *confident.* The tone shows the author's praise for Ms. Paul.

3. Answers will vary. Alice Paul watched as many suffragists peacefully marched toward the Capitol building. These women were marching to bring about public awareness and support for women's suffrage.

4. Answers will vary.

5. Answers will vary.

Page 74

1. The life of a suffragette was very difficult. Suffragettes endured arrest, prison, and forced feeding to name just a few of their sacrifices.

2. Her use of *thee* and *thy* are the pronouns used by Quakers in place of the more common *you* and *your.*

3. Among other things, Alice Paul was brave, strong willed and caring. (She didn't want her mother to worry.)

4. Answers will vary. At that period in history many people were jailed for "being a public nuisance."

Page 75

1. The Capitol dome and the red, white, and blue ribbons symbolize America. The trumpet might represent the suffragettes' perseverance in getting their message known.

2. The messages are both visual and verbal.

3. The women are summoning all to join their cause.

4. Answers will vary, but the women seem to have confidence and to feel positive about what they are doing.

Page 76

Top

1. The term "Kaiser" is the title of the leader of Germany. It was insulting to call the leader of a democratic nation this. The poster is showing President Wilson as a hypocrite because Wilson had criticized the government of Germany for denying voting rights.

2. It says that 20 million American women were being denied the right to vote. We can infer that President Wilson was against an amendment that would have given women the right to vote.

Bottom

1. The following questions are asked: How long must women wait for liberty? What will you do for woman suffrage?

2. They look serious. They are not chatting, but standing almost at attention. The 9 women have made an attempt to dress alike: uniformity in dress as well as philosophy. Each is wearing a banner identifying the college or university she attends. They have signs and banners to call attention to themselves in front of the fence of the White House.

3. The importance of the photographs is to document the struggle that women had to win the right to vote. They show that women were serious about their desire to vote and willing to inconvenience themselves in order to achieve their goal.

Page 77

1. Answers will vary, but today it is taken for granted that women can vote and attend school. However, today it is not assumed that the main reason to educate women is so they will become good mothers. People still believe that children are influenced by their mothers, but there are probably more outside influences today than there were in 1917.
2. Answers will vary.
3. Answers will vary.

Page 78

1. This is a letter.
2. The letter is encouraging each receiver to sell five tickets to a baseball game in order to raise funds for their organization.
3. The baseball game was sponsored by the Women's Political Union of New Jersey.
4. Answers will vary, but may include the following: Ladies will not have to pay. They will make a profit of 10 cents and 25 cents on each ticket sold. This is the biggest fund-raising opportunity of the year for the group. Notable suffrage speakers will address the men.
5. Answers will vary, but may include the following: Apparently baseball was popular. Crowds of 10 to 30 thousand people were not uncommon at big events. People were interested in automobiles.

Page 79

1. This resolution was made May 19,1919.
2. The resolution was passed on August 26, 1920. It took about 15 months.
3. Three fourths of state legislatures had to ratify the resolution in order for it to become an amendment to the Constitution.
4. Wisconsin, Illinois and Michigan were the first to ratify; they did so on June 10, 1919. Many votes were taken. Some states refused to ratify it and later changed their votes. This amendment was specifically rejected by Georgia, Alabama, South Carolina, Virginia, Maryland, Mississippi, Delaware, and Louisiana. However, all the states eventually ratified it. The amendment became official when Tennessee ratified it. This is the order in which the first 36 ratified it:

1.	Wisconsin (June 10, 1919)	19.	Maine (November 5, 1919)
2.	Illinois (June 10, 1919, reaffirmed on June 17, 1919)	20.	North Dakota (December 1, 1919)
3.	Michigan (June 10, 1919)	21.	South Dakota (December 4, 1919)
4.	Kansas (June 16, 1919)	22.	Colorado (December 15, 1919)
5.	New York (June 16, 1919)	23.	Kentucky (January 6, 1920)
6.	Ohio (June 16, 1919)	24.	Rhode Island (January 6, 1920)
7.	Pennsylvania (June 24, 1919)	25.	Oregon (January 13, 1920)
8.	Massachusetts (June 25, 1919)	26.	Indiana (January 16, 1920)
9.	Texas (June 28, 1919)	27.	Wyoming (January 27, 1920)
10.	Iowa (July 2, 1919)[4]	28.	Nevada (February 7, 1920)
11.	Missouri (July 3, 1919)	29.	New Jersey (February 9, 1920)
12.	Arkansas (July 28, 1919)	30.	Idaho (February 11, 1920)
13.	Montana (August 2, 1919)[4]	31.	Arizona (February 12, 1920)
14.	Nebraska (August 2, 1919)	32.	New Mexico (February 21, 1920)
15.	Minnesota (September 8, 1919)	33.	Oklahoma (February 28, 1920)
16.	New Hampshire (September 10, 1919)	34.	West Virginia (March 10, 1920, confirmed on Sept. 21, 1920)
17.	Utah (October 2, 1919)	35.	Washington (March 22, 1920)
18.	California (November 1, 1919)	36.	Tennessee (August 18, 1920)

5. Answers will vary.

Bibliography

Bailyn, Bernard. *Faces of the Revolution.* New York: Alfred Knopf, 1990.

Blumberg, Rhoda. *The Great American Gold Rush.* New York: Bradbury Press, 1989.

Burns, Ken and Duncan, Dayton. *Lewis and Clark—The Journey of the Corps of Discovery.* New York: Alfred Knopf, 1997.

Canfield, Cass. *Sam Adams's Revolution.* New York: Harper & Row, 1976.

deVoto, Bernard. *The Journals of Lewis and Clark.* Boston: Houghton Mifflin Co., 1953.

Fischer, David H. *Paul Revere's Ride.* New York: Oxford University Press, 1994.

Harper, Robert W. *Old Gloucester County & The American Revolution.* Woodbury, New Jersey: Gloucester County Cultural and Heritage Commission, 1986.

Hewitt, James, Editor. *The Old West, The Trailblazers.* New York: Time Life Books, 1973.

Irwin, Inez. *The Story of Alice Paul.* Fairfax, Virginia: Denlinger's, 1977.

Moynihan, Ruth. *So Much to be Done.* Lincoln, Nebraska: Nebraska University Press, 1990.

Internet Resources:
www.oregontrail.com
www.earlyamerica.com
www.archives.gov
www.americanwest.com
www.womenshistory.about.com
www.history.navy.mil
www.ushistory.org
http://odur.let.rug.nl/usa
www.seacoastnh.com
http://www.teachersfirst.com/ushistory
http://www.greatwomen.org
http://lcweb.loc.gov/rr/print/catalog.html